Cassell's Rural Science Series

D0192345

Environmental Science

Bernard Salt

Head of Rural and Environmental Science,
King Edward VI School, Lichfield
Chief Examiner, West Midlands Examination Board

Cassell

CASSELL LTD
1 St Anne's Road
Eastbourne, East Sussex, BN21 3UN

First published 1982
Second impression 1984

ISBN 0 304 30784 X

Filmset in Great Britain by
Northumberland Press Ltd., Gateshead, Tyne and Wear
Printed and bound in Hungary

Contents

Preface

This book is intended for pupils who are working towards an external examination in Environmental Science.

A few topics are, of necessity, dealt with on a world basis but most are confined to a local level in order to allow a high proportion of practical work and to give pupils materials to which they can easily relate. All the practical work has been thoroughly tested in the teaching situation and can be undertaken with confidence. The village study can be adapted easily to the study of a suburb where this would be more convenient.

Water has been used to introduce some scientific concepts which are basic to the subject; this has made the chapter rather comprehensive and it should be studied early in the course. For the convenience of packaging, conservation appears at the end of the book; material from this chapter should however be introduced at all stages so pupils gradually develop a conservation ethic.

I am grateful to Mr W. Jackson BA for his assistance with the *Key to Rock Types*; when using this key, pupils should be given typical examples of the rocks it includes.

The in-text questions are included to reinforce learning and pupils should be encouraged to check their mental answers with those at the end of the book before proceeding with the text. Pupils should also be referred to the glossary until they make use of it without prompting. Question one, at the end of each chapter, is a straightforward comprehension while the others are similar to those set by external examiners.

This subject deals with areas where there is likely to be some controversy; I have deliberately confined myself to factual material which I hope will be the basis for some spirited classroom debates as pupils begin to realise it is *their* world they are studying.

Bernard Salt
Lichfield 1982

Acknowledgements

The author and publishers would like to thank the following sources who have kindly supplied illustrative material: Barnaby's Picture Library; British Telecom; Crittall Warmlife Ltd; Central Electricity Generating Board; Esso Petroleum; Farmers Weekly; The Lichfield Mercury; Nature Conservancy Council; Severn Trent Water Authority; Staffordshire County Council; Jeff Foott, Survival Anglia and John Topham Picture Library.

Photographs (original prints) by Will Carnell.
Manuscript typed by Big I.

Cover photograph

The photograph shows the Swallowtail butterfly. This is an *endangered species* which means that it may soon be extinct as man's activities are destroying its natural habitat. The photograph is reproduced by kind permission of John Mason of the Nature Conservancy Council.

1 The world in space

The sun and planets

The universe consists of many groups of stars called *galaxies*. One galaxy, the Milky Way, contains a star which we call the sun. Like many other stars, the sun is a huge mass of gas where thermo-nuclear reactions are taking place, converting hydrogen atoms to helium; the matter lost during these reactions is converted to energy. This energy travels as electro-magnetic waves, and a tiny proportion of it reaches the earth as light and heat.

Nine planets orbit the sun. They are Earth, Jupiter, Mars, Mercury, Neptune, Pluto, Saturn, Uranus, and Venus. They all orbit in the same direction and almost in the same plane. The four planets nearest the sun are small (diameter less than 13 000 km) and rocky, and the others are large (diameters over 44 000 km) and of low density. The exception is Pluto, which has a diameter of only 6000 km.

Task 1.1

Write out the list of planets in the order of increasing distance from the sun. The figures in brackets give the distance between the planet and the sun

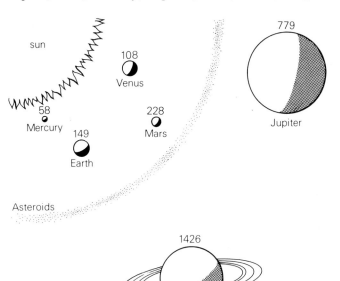

The planets (figures are average distances from the sun in millions of kms)

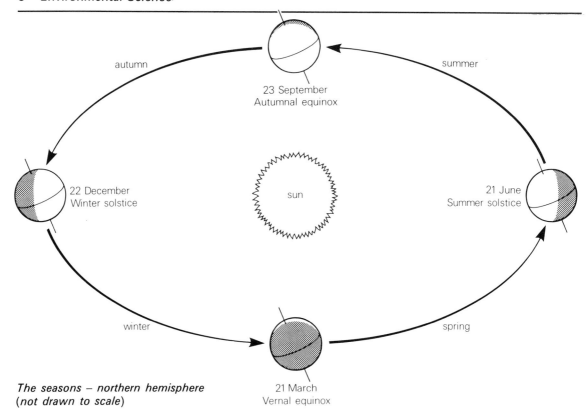

The seasons – northern hemisphere
(*not drawn to scale*)

autumn

23 September
Autumnal equinox

summer

22 December
Winter solstice

sun

21 June
Summer solstice

winter

spring

21 March
Vernal equinox

in astronomical units (one astronomical unit is equal to the mean distance of the earth from the sun, 149.6 million kilometres): Earth (1.0), Jupiter (5.2), Mars (1.52), Mercury (0.39), Neptune (30.06), Pluto (32.44), Saturn (9.54), Uranus (19.10), Venus (0.72).

Between Jupiter and Mars there is a belt of thousands of small bodies called *asteroids* which orbit the sun, and which could be the remains of planets that have broken up. Studies of the trajectories (paths) of meteorites entering the atmosphere indicate that many of them fall from this asteroid belt.

The earth

Earth is the only planet capable of supporting life as we know it; other planets are either too hot, too cold, without water, or their atmospheres are unsuitable to support life.

What is the composition of the earth's atmosphere?
... Q.1

American space probes suggest that there are no other life forms on other planets.

The earth takes approximately $365\frac{1}{4}$ days to orbit the sun. There are 365 days in a year; what happens to the extra quarter of a day? **... Q.2**

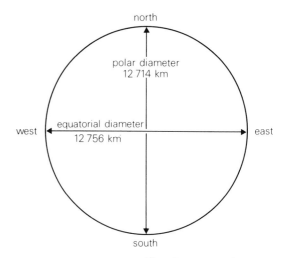

north

polar diameter
12 714 km

west

equatorial diameter
12 756 km

east

south

The diameters of the earth

In addition to orbiting around the sun, the earth is also spinning on an axis, the ends of which we call the *north* and *south poles*. The rotation of the earth has helped to form its shape as the spin has caused the middle to bulge. A shape like this is called an *oblate spheroid*.

Day and night

The rotation also causes day and night:

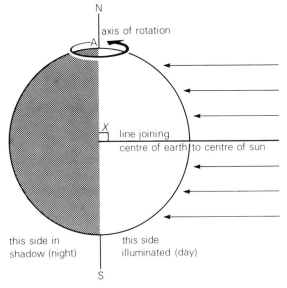

Twice each year the angle 'X' above is 90° giving night and day of equal length

How can you check, from your own observations, that the arrow marked 'A' is pointing in the correct direction?
... Q.3

As the earth is illuminated from one direction only, at any given time, part of it is in darkness and part in light. As the earth rotates, areas get alternate periods of illumination and darkness, giving day and night. The time taken for the earth to complete one rotation is divided into 24 hours. On 21 June and 22 December the earth is in the positions shown below.

If the earth's axis of rotation was at right angles to an imaginary line joining the centre of the earth to the centre of the sun, days and nights would be of equal length. In fact, the earth's axis is tilted at an angle, and for six months the days are longer than the nights in the northern hemisphere; then for the next six months the days are longer than the nights in the southern hemisphere. As you are aware from your own observations, day length does not suddenly change – it is a gradual process. This changing day length gives most parts of the world its seasons – its winters and its summers, with their corresponding effects upon plant and animal life. On two days every year, day and night are of equal length (12 hours); such a day is called an *equinox*.

On what days in the year does an equinox occur?
... Q.4

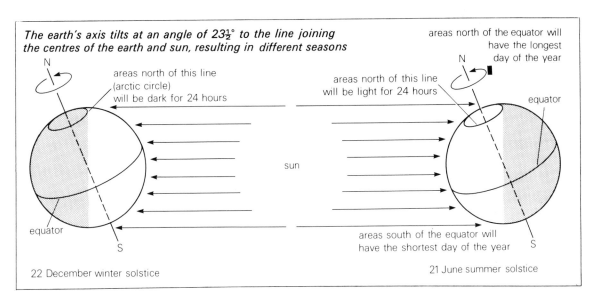

Temperature

This explains why the summer days are longer than the winter days, but not why they are warmer. The reasons why it is generally warm in summer and cold in winter are:

1. When one part of the earth passes through a summer, it has a longer period of warming and a shorter period of cooling than it does in the winter.
2. The sun's rays fall on a smaller area because the earth's surface is inclined at a different angle to the sun's rays in summer.

3. The sun's rays must pass through more atmosphere in winter than in summer.

Where will the sun be directly overhead at midday on 22 December? ... **Q.5**
What will be the period of daylight north of the Arctic Circle on 22 December? ... **Q.6**

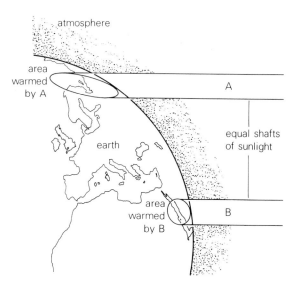

Because equal amounts of radiation warm different areas of the earth's surface at different latitudes, the temperatures will be different giving the world various temperature zones

The moon

The earth has one satellite – the moon – which has a diameter of 3500 km. The moon orbits the earth every 27¼ days and reflects some of the sun's light to the world. This light is very weak but gives some visibility on cloudless nights.

On earth we only ever see one face of the moon. Why is this? ... **Q.7**

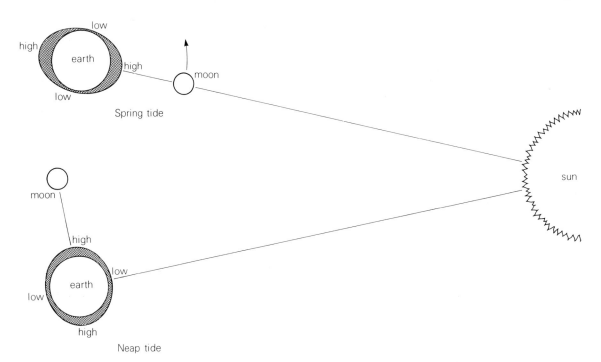

Tides

An important effect the moon has upon earth is to raise *tides*. Both the sun and the moon exert a gravitational pull upon the earth – even rocks move very slightly in response to this pull. But water, being free to move, piles up to give a tide. Lunar (moon) tides are much higher than those caused by the sun as the moon is very much nearer to the earth.

The diagram shows that there is a corresponding high tide on the opposite side of the world – there are two high tides during a twenty-four hour period.

When the sun and the moon pull together, as they do at *new moon* and *full moon*, the tide is a little higher; these tides are known as *spring tides*. At the first and third quarter of the moon's phases, the sun and the moon pull in opposite directions and the high tide is lower than normal; these tides are known as *neap tides*.

Locally, tides are complicated by the shape of the coastline and the nature of water currents; these affect the actual time the tide reaches its highest point. The moon also raises tides in the atmosphere, but no effects of this are felt on the surface of the earth.

Atmosphere

An integral part of the earth is the layer of gas which surrounds the solid and liquid matter. We cannot see this gas but we can certainly feel it and continually extract oxygen from it and return carbon dioxide to it. Like other matter, gas is subject to the force of gravity and it is gravity which holds it in place, preventing it from escaping into outer space. The gas which surrounds the world is called *atmosphere*; it is not a single gas but is a mixture of several. The most abundant gas in the atmosphere is *nitrogen* (78%), the second is *oxygen* (21%); the other 1% consists of *argon* (0.9%), *carbon dioxide* (0.03%), and a few gases like *neon* of which there are only traces. The atmosphere also contains water vapour in varying amounts.

The air on the earth's surface is compressed by the air above. Higher in the atmosphere there is

less gas above and the pressure decreases. The decrease in pressure means that there is less gas in an equal space and so less oxygen to breathe, which is why many expeditions up high mountains take a supply of oxygen with them. The atmosphere extends to heights of over 60 km above the earth, but it is very sparse at these heights and 99% of it is below half this height, i.e., below 30 km.

Layers of the atmosphere

The collection of gases nearest the earth is called the *troposphere*. In the troposphere, the higher one goes the colder it becomes. The effects of this can be seen in mountainous areas where crops may be grown in the valleys when the mountain tops are covered with snow. This temperature gradient occurs because the sun's radiation passes through the troposphere without being absorbed; on reaching the surface of the earth, some of the radiation is absorbed, warming it, and the atmosphere is in turn warmed by the warm earth.

At a height of 16 km the temperature of the atmosphere is $-80\,°C$. Here atmospheric temperature begins to *increase* with height; this area is known as the *tropopause* and marks the end of the troposphere.

In the region of the tropopause some of the atmospheric oxygen (O_2) changes to ozone (O_3). The *ozone layer*, as it is called, absorbs ultra-violet radiation from the sun's radiation, releasing its energy and raising the temperature of the atmosphere. The action of ozone is of very great importance, as if this ultra-violet light reached the earth it would destroy all life. The amount of ozone is very small – if it were possible to put the ozone on the surface of the earth it would make a layer only 3 mm thick. The use of aerosols could reduce the ozone layer (see page 104) with disastrous effects on life on earth.

At heights greater than 50 km there is only a very small amount of gas, much of which becomes *ionised* (atoms gain or lose electrons) by high-energy radiation. The ionised layer, called the *ionosphere*, reflects some radio waves back to earth, making long-distance radio communication possible.

The earth's atmosphere

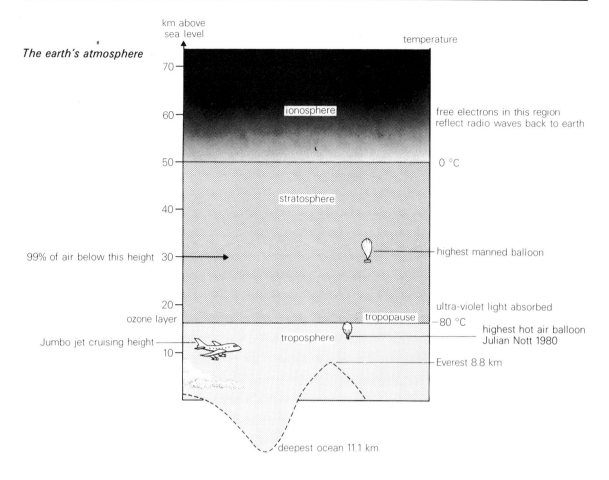

- km above sea level
- temperature
- ionosphere — free electrons in this region reflect radio waves back to earth
- 70
- 60
- 50 — 0 °C
- stratosphere
- 40
- 99% of air below this height — 30 — highest manned balloon
- 20 — ultra-violet light absorbed
- ozone layer — tropopause — −80 °C — highest hot air balloon Julian Nott 1980
- Jumbo jet cruising height — troposphere
- 10 — Everest 8.8 km
- deepest ocean 11.1 km

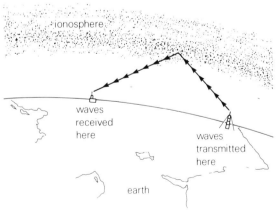

- ionosphere
- waves received here
- waves transmitted here
- earth

Air movements in the atmosphere

We have seen that the troposphere is transparent to the sun's radiation. This would always be true if there were no *clouds*. In certain conditions the small amount of water vapour in the atmosphere condenses into very small particles of water which remain suspended in the atmosphere as cloud. Cloud prevents some of the sun's radiation from reaching the earth (think how cool it goes when a cloud covers the sun while you are sunbathing),

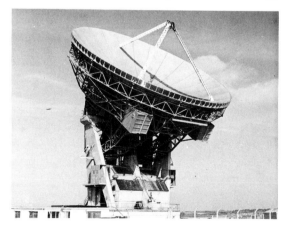

Radio receiver station

making the earth cooler than it would otherwise be. Some of the sun's radiation is reflected from the cloud and some is scattered into different directions by the water droplets which form the cloud.

At night, however, clouds act like a huge blanket, keeping the earth warmer than it would otherwise be (late spring frosts occur only on cloudless nights). Clouds move with the atmosphere and bring water from sea to land. Next time you see a cloud moving across the sky, remember that the cloud is *not* floating through the atmosphere but the *whole of the atmosphere at that point is moving*, the cloud is the only part you can *see* as the rest is transparent. Atmospheric movements on the surface of the earth are felt as *wind*, but these movements are very small compared with the movements in the upper atmosphere. It is the movements in the atmosphere which cause weather and bring water to the land, shaping the earth and creating the environment.

Convection currents

Convection currents can be observed using the apparatus* below:

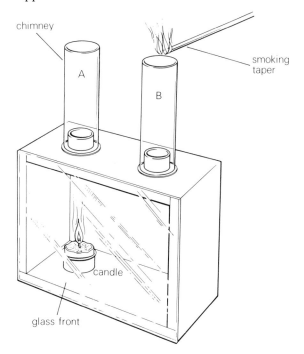

* Available from Griffin and George or Philip Harris or made from an aquarium tank and some sheets of cartridge paper.

The candle is lit and a piece of smouldering string is held over chimney B. Smoke is seen to descend chimney B and ascend chimney A.

In the same way, convection currents are created in the atmosphere – the warmed air becomes less dense and therefore rises to be replaced by colder air. This is one of the causes of air movements which help to shape our weather. In the UK, south-west winds bring warm moist air from the Atlantic, which makes the western part of the country warmer and wetter than the eastern part (weather recording – see *Rural Science 1*).

The internal structure of the earth

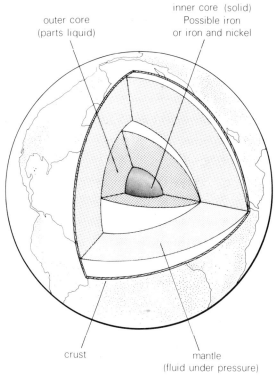

Although man has walked on the moon and sent exploratory vehicles to other planets in the solar system, he has not penetrated very far into the earth. If the world were represented by a balloon 400 mm in diameter, the deepest working made by man on the same scale would not release the air from the balloon. The diagram above shows a section through the centre of the earth.

Man's knowledge about the inside of the earth has been built up by three main methods:

1. Recording and analysis of the passage of shock waves through the centre of the earth and around the earth's crust, after an earthquake or atomic explosion. The instruments which record wave motions in the earth's crust are called *seismometers*.
2. Analysis of the composition and structure of meteorites which fall to earth from asteroids.
3. Analysis of material brought from great depths by volcanoes.

Tectonic plates

The earth's crust is not of uniform thickness – it consists of a number of huge plates, *tectonic plates*, which move very slowly (perhaps only 10 mm a year) on the earth's mantle (directly below the crust). When two plates move apart, the gap is filled by new material rising from the mantle and solidifying.

When two plates meet, one may be forced down below the other into the mantle. Some of the rocks will change form because of heat and pressure and some may become molten and form mantle material. Pressures created by tectonic plate movements push folds of the crust upwards, forming mountains:

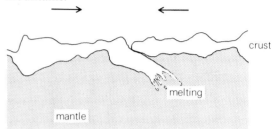

Earthquakes

When one plate presses against another, pressure builds up until the plates may slip, this slip being felt as an earthquake. Earthquakes occur on the edge of tectonic plates and a map of earthquakes recorded over a number of years indicates the position of these plates:

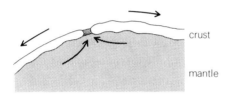

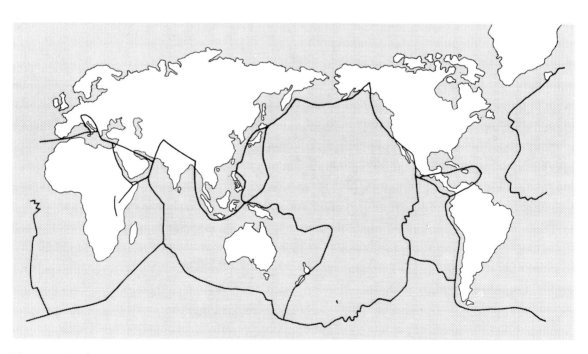

The tectonic plates

Volcanoes

Volcanoes are also likely to occur along the edge of a tectonic plate; volcanoes are caused by molten material rising from the mantle and then solidifying.

When there is a violent volcanic eruption, many tonnes of ash may be thrown high into the atmosphere. This ash could stop some solar radiation reaching the earth and this may have an effect upon the weather.

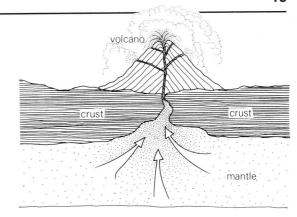

Questions: The world in space

1. Write single sentences to answer the following questions.
   (a) What is a galaxy?
   (b) Explain the term 'oblate spheroid'.
   (c) How many high tides occur during a twenty-four hour period?
   (d) Why is there less oxygen available at the top of a mountain than at the bottom?
   (e) Which gas in the atmosphere protects the earth from ultraviolet radiation?
   (f) What natural disasters are likely to occur along the edges of a tectonic plate?
   (g) Why is a spring tide higher than a neap tide?

2. With the aid of diagrams describe the effects on the earth of
   (a) the world revolving about its own axis.
   (b) the world orbiting around the sun.

3. Explain why it is winter in the UK at the same time that it is summer in New Zealand. Support your answer with a diagram.

4. Draw a diagram to show a section through the centre of the earth. Label the various layers. What effects (if any) do the layers beneath the crust have on life on earth?

5. Explain why:
   (a) a balloon intended to rise several kilometers is not fully inflated before being released into the atmosphere.
   (b) the temperature is higher above the tropopause than it is below it.
   (c) radio waves can be sent to places beyond the horizon.

2 Rocks and minerals

Rock types

The rocks forming the earth's crust can be classified into three groups according to how they were formed. These are:

1. Igneous rocks

When material from the earth's mantle cools and solidifies, the rock which forms is *igneous*. Examples include gabbro, basalt and granite.

2. Sedimentary rocks

Tiny fragments of rock (and other materials) are carried by moving water. When the water slows down, or stops, the fragments sink to the bottom as sediment. Large sediments eventually solidify into rock and the different sediment layers (bedding) can be seen in the rock. A typical sedimentary rock is sandstone. Water also deposits other materials which eventually form sedimentary rocks, such as limestone (see page 20).

3. Metamorphic rocks

Sedimentary rocks may become buried and subjected to great pressure and heat. Sometimes these external forces cause chemical and physical changes in the rocks and their form changes, for example, shale becomes slate and limestone becomes marble. The rocks formed as a result of these changes are called **metamorphic** rocks.

What kind of rock does volcanic lava become as it solidifies? ... Q.1

Rock formation

When it was formed, the earth did not cool over a short period of time, leaving a uniform crust on its surface like the ice on a pond. The first rocks were formed over 4000 million years ago and the process has continued to this day. It is such a slow process that we are not aware of it except when there is an earthquake or a volcano. Some of the rock formed 4000 million years ago remains, some has been converted into other rocks and some has been forced back into the mantle where it has possibly melted down.

Continents slowly move on the surface of the earth. Some rock is buckled and forced upwards to form mountains, while some is forced downwards and subjected to great heat and pressure, changing from igneous or sedimentary into metamorphic.

Geological periods

Just as historians divide the past into 'ages', the Stone Age, the Bronze Age, the Iron Age and so on, the geologists also divide the past into ages. The geologists' ages are very much longer than the historians' ages – they measure their time in millions of years (see page 16).

Some of the geologists' periods are of very great importance today, e.g., the coal seams which were produced during the Carboniferous age. The British Isles are on the edge of a continent and have been subject to much geological change during the last 600 million years. As a result a lot of different types of rock outcrop (appear at the surface), giving the islands a great variety of landscapes, soils, vegetation and minerals.

Key for identification of some common rocks

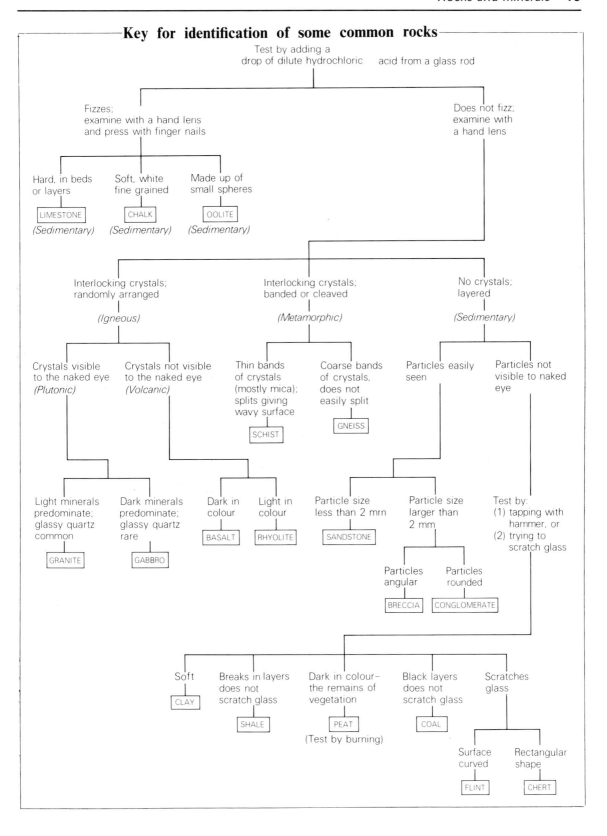

Test by adding a drop of dilute hydrochloric acid from a glass rod

Fizzes; examine with a hand lens and press with finger nails

- Hard, in beds or layers
  - LIMESTONE
  - *(Sedimentary)*
- Soft, white fine grained
  - CHALK
  - *(Sedimentary)*
- Made up of small spheres
  - OOLITE
  - *(Sedimentary)*

Does not fizz; examine with a hand lens

- Interlocking crystals; randomly arranged *(Igneous)*
  - Crystals visible to the naked eye *(Plutonic)*
    - Light minerals predominate; glassy quartz common
      - GRANITE
    - Dark minerals predominate; glassy quartz rare
      - GABBRO
  - Crystals not visible to the naked eye *(Volcanic)*
    - Dark in colour
      - BASALT
    - Light in colour
      - RHYOLITE

- Interlocking crystals; banded or cleaved *(Metamorphic)*
  - Thin bands of crystals (mostly mica); splits giving wavy surface
    - SCHIST
  - Coarse bands of crystals, does not easily split
    - GNEISS

- No crystals; layered *(Sedimentary)*
  - Particles easily seen
    - Particle size less than 2 mm
      - SANDSTONE
    - Particle size larger than 2 mm
      - Particles angular
        - BRECCIA
      - Particles rounded
        - CONGLOMERATE
  - Particles not visible to naked eye
    - Test by:
      (1) tapping with hammer, or
      (2) trying to scratch glass
      - Soft
        - CLAY
      - Breaks in layers does not scratch glass
        - SHALE
      - Dark in colour– the remains of vegetation
        - PEAT
        - (Test by burning)
      - Black layers does not scratch glass
        - COAL
      - Scratches glass
        - Surface curved
          - FLINT
        - Rectangular shape
          - CHERT

PERIOD	millions of years ago	FAUNA
Tertiary		
Cretaceous	100	
Jurassic		
Triassic	200	
Permian		
Carboniferous	300	
Devonian		
Silurian	400	
Ordovician		
	500	
Cambrian		
	600	
Precambrian		
	3000	

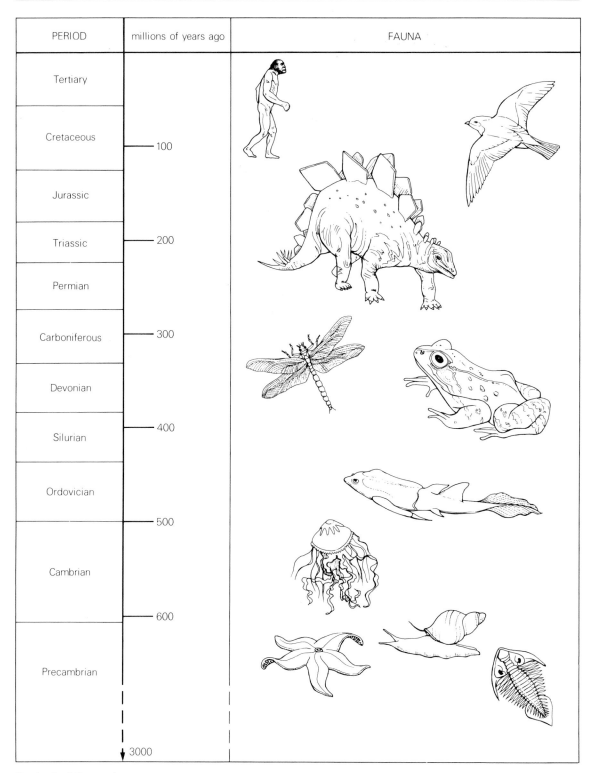

Geological timescale

Minerals

The world contains 103 different elements; a few of these are in the air, some in organic matter, two in water (H_2O), which also contains some dissolved substances, and the rest in rocks as *minerals*, which are the naturally formed chemical compounds which make up rocks. Some elements are present in large quantities – only eight elements make up 99% of the earth's crust:

Element	Percentage of earth's crust (by weight)
oxygen	48
silicon	28
aluminium	8
iron	5
calcium	3.5
sodium	2.8
potassium	2.6
magnesium	2

Others are present in very small quantities, e.g., the precious metals (gold, silver, platinum) and the rare gases of the atmosphere (neon and argon). Air, minerals, water and organic matter are all man has from which to make the 'things' he requires.

A lot of energy and thousands of litres of water are used in manufacture: in addition this car will consume 16 000 litres of petrol before it goes to the scrapyard.

15 tonnes of material have to be extracted from the earth's crust to support the lifestyle of every person in this country. This material includes:

   2500 kg of stones/sand/gravel;
   500 kg of steel;
   200 kg of cement;
   70 kg of clay; and
   6 kg of lead.

Some of the materials are imported and some are home produced; quantities of minerals extracted in the UK in a single recent year are shown in the diagram overleaf.

What substance is extracted from the earth in very large quantities which is not included in the diagram overleaf? ... Q.2

In which county is most of the china-clay produced? ...Q.3

Use of the earth's resources

The 'things' of modern society use up a lot of material resources. The average European car weighs 900 kg and contains:

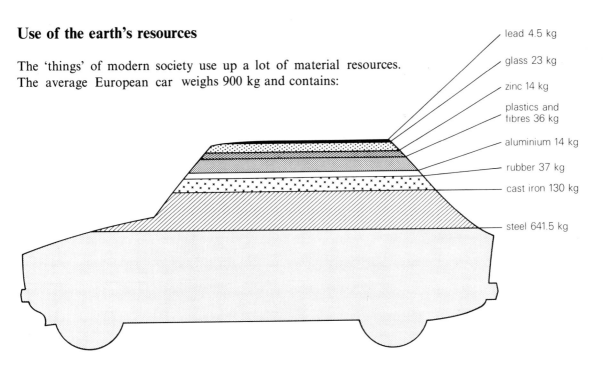

lead 4.5 kg
glass 23 kg
zinc 14 kg
plastics and fibres 36 kg
aluminium 14 kg
rubber 37 kg
cast iron 130 kg
steel 641.5 kg

Production of minerals during a recent year in the United Kingdom – tonnes

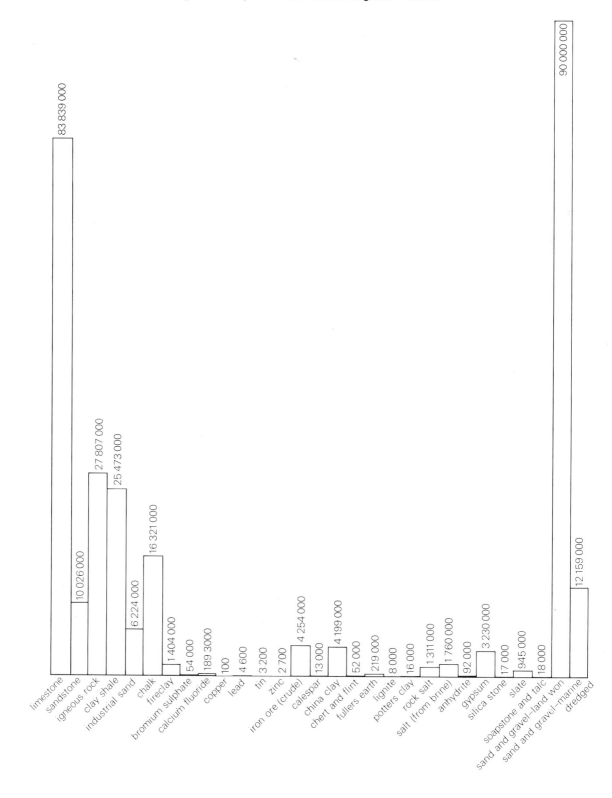

'Spaceship earth'

The earth is rather like a very large spaceship – in a spaceship there is only a certain quantity of each material and once a material has been used there can be no more unless the spaceship returns to base to collect it. The earth cannot return to base and although there is much more material in the earth than there is in a spaceship there are also a lot more people! At present rates of extrac-tion, and if no more deposits are found, the world will run out of some materials quite soon.

Task 2.1

Study the chart below. Then copy it out and complete the last column.

Metal	World reserves (millions of tonnes)	Amount used world wide each year (millions of tonnes)	Number of years'
Iron	91 000	800	
Aluminium	4 150	12	
Copper	364	8	
Zinc	306	4.5	
Lead	94	4	

Locally, many materials have already been exhausted:

A derelict copper mine

Recycling

Less materials would have to be extracted and the world reserves would last much longer if they were *recycled* (old scrap materials reclaimed and used again). Some materials, especially metals, are used many times over and scrap-metal merchants make a living by buying, sorting and selling metals which can be used again (see page 127). The proportion of scrap which is recycled in the UK is:

aluminium	45%
copper	40%
iron	55%
lead	60%
zinc	30%

Whether or not a mineral element is recycled depends very much upon the availability of the waste from which it is derived – lead is easily recovered from old car batteries but the lead added to petrol is emitted with the exhaust gases and is lost forever. Economics play a crucial role in recycling – if an element is very rare and expensive it is much more likely to be recycled than if it is plentiful and cheap; thus almost 90% of all 'waste' gold is recycled.

Collection and reprocessing of used materials can use a lot of energy and recycling is sometimes more expensive than extraction from the ore.

Extraction and use of a non-metal – limestone

When a marine animal dies, the hard parts (such as the shell and skeleton) sink to the bottom of the sea. These hard parts are made up of insoluble calcium carbonate. 300 million years ago there was a warm sea where this country now is. The skeletons and shells of sea-dwelling creatures were deposited at the rate of about 10 mm per century, and over millions of years very thick layers were formed.

What thickness would form in 1 000 000 years?
... Q.4

Later these deposits were covered with other materials and became compacted into rocks, then massive movements of the earth's crust during a mountain-building period pushed the rocks above the level of the sea. Later still, upper layers were removed by erosion, exposing the ancient calcium carbonate deposits. These deposits vary in form and may be chalk, limestone or marble rocks. One such deposit exists near the Peak District at Buxton and it is being worked by ICI Ltd, who extract 6 000 000 tonnes of lime from it each year. Extraction is by quarrying:

Holes are drilled and filled with explosives each week.

The explosion blasts down hundreds of tonnes of rock (98% calcium carbonate) which is loaded into lorries with a mechanical shovel for transport to a huge crushing machine.

Uses of limestone

Limestone is crushed and used for road building, and on other sites where a hard base is required.

Limestone is also roasted in kilns at 2100 °C and the following reaction takes place:

$$CaCO_3 \rightarrow CaO + CO_2$$
(calcium   (calcium   (carbon
carbonate)   oxide)   dioxide)

The calcium oxide (*quicklime*) which is formed has many industrial uses.

Investigation 2.1

(*Wear goggles*)
Using tongs, take a lump (about 20 g) of calcium oxide from its jar and place it on a metal tray. Pour on 10 ml of water and observe. The calcium oxide warms, expands, cracks and crumbles as it changes into calcium hydroxide (slaked lime).

$$CaO + H_2O \rightarrow Ca(OH)_2 + heat$$
(quicklime) (water)   (slaked lime)

(A chemical reaction which produces heat is called an *exothermic* reaction.)
Calcium hydroxide is the lime of limewater which turns milky in the presence of carbon dioxide:

$$Ca(OH)_2 + CO_2 \rightarrow CaCO_3 + H_2O$$
(calcium   (carbon   (calcium   (water)
hydroxide) dioxide)   carbonate)

As calcium carbonate is insoluble it precipitates, making the solution appear milky.

Task 2.2

1. Place about 100 ml of clay soil in each of two glass jars A and B and two-thirds fill each with water (as shown in the diagram).
2. Cover each jar and shake vigorously until the water is clouded with a suspension of clay particles.
3. Add 50 ml lime water to jar A.
4. Add 50 ml distilled water to jar B.
5. Allow the jars to stand and observe the clay suspension in each. In jar A, crumbs of clay will be seen to form. These quickly sink, clearing the water – this is known as *flocculation*. There is no flocculation in jar B, and the water will remain clouded for many hours.

Lime has many uses in industry as a cheap alkali to neutralise acids. It is also used in sewage works to remove suspended solids from water (by flocculation).

Millions of tonnes of lime are spread on the land each year, to reduce soil acidity, improve soil structure, and supply the element calcium which is necessary for plant growth.

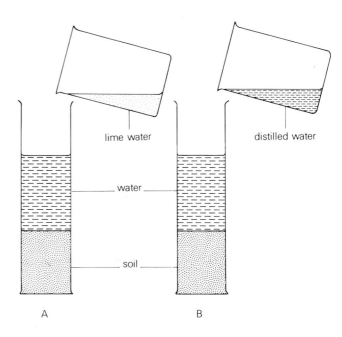

The dust from limestone crushing plants is mixed with silica-sand and gypsum ($CaSO_4$) and processed into cement for building.

A spoil heap

amounts of waste which have to be disposed of; their extraction makes large holes in the ground and uses more energy as more material has to be moved.

A disused quarry

Extraction and use of a metal – iron

Over 90% of all metal used by man is iron – it is a very important metal. *Steel* is iron which contains a small quantity of carbon.

Which of the following do not depend upon iron: railways, roads, wheat production, plastic light fittings, concrete buildings, coal mining, joinery? ... Q.5

Iron occurs in the earth's crust in igneous rocks as magnetite (Fe_2O_4) and haematite (Fe_2O_3). Some iron also occurs in sedimentary rocks and is quarried in Lincolnshire and Northamptonshire, but most of the iron ore used in the UK is imported high-grade ore (i.e. the ore has a high iron content) of up to 60% iron. The British ores are low-grade and contain only 25% iron. Use of low-grade ores results in the production of large

Extraction of iron from its ore

Some modern extraction plants have a steel-making plant on the same site, and freshly extracted iron (pig-iron) is immediately converted to steel, saving on cost of transport and reheating.

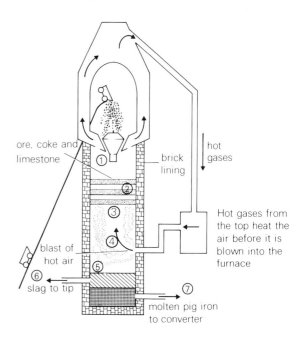

Iron is extracted from its ore in a blast furnace:

Iron ore, coke and limestone are fed into the top of the blast furnace, parts of which are at temperatures in excess of 1400 °C. Inside the furnace, the following reactions take place:

1. Coke is burned, producing carbon dioxide:

$$C \ + \ O_2 \ \rightarrow \ CO_2$$
(carbon)　(oxygen)　(carbon dioxide)

2. Because the temperature is so high, the carbon dioxide reacts with more coke to form carbon monoxide:

$$CO_2 \ + \ C \ \rightarrow \ 2CO$$
(carbon (carbon) (carbon
dioxide) monoxide)

3. Carbon monoxide reacts with the iron ore, releasing metallic iron which runs to the bottom of the furnace:

$$Fe_2O_3 \ + \ 3CO \ \rightarrow \ 2Fe \ + \ 3CO_2$$
(ferric (carbon (iron) (carbon
oxide) monoxide) dioxide)

4. Meanwhile the limestone (which has been added to remove impurities) decomposes to form quicklime and carbon dioxide:

$$CaCO_3 \ \rightarrow \ CaO \ + \ CO_2$$
(calcium (calcium (carbon
carbonate) oxide) dioxide)

5. The quicklime reacts with the sand, forming slag (calcium silicate):

$$CaO \ + \ SiO_2 \ \rightarrow \ CaSiO_3$$
(calcium (silicon (calcium
oxide) oxide) silicate)

6. As slag is lighter than iron, it floats to the top and is drawn off to a *slag heap* to cool and be stored until it is required for road building.

7. The molten iron (which has a 5% carbon content) is run into a rotating converter where most of the carbon is removed by blowing in oxygen and steam. The resulting product is *steel*, the properties of which can be changed by adding small quantities of other elements to form alloys:

Element added	Property	Use
carbon (1%)	hard	cutting tools
manganese	very hard	high grade cutting tools
chromium	stainless	cutlery and surgical instruments

Extraction and use of a metal – aluminium

Aluminium is a metal which man only began to exploit this century and he is finding many new uses for it. Aluminium does not rust and it has a high strength–weight ratio, making it an ideal metal for aeroplane construction. Aluminium can be moulded (engine blocks), extruded (window frames), rolled into very thin sheets (cooking foil) and spun into shapes (saucepans). In addition to its many industrial uses, the importance of this metal can be seen around the home – it is used for milk bottle tops, ring pulls for tinned drinks, foil wrappings for chocolate, frames for patio doors and glazing bars for greenhouses. Aluminium is a very abundant element and occurs in clay, but it is not possible to extract it from this source. In some parts of the world, including Jamaica, France, America and Africa, aluminium occurs as an oxide (Al_2O_3) in large surface deposits of a mineral ore called *bauxite*. It is extracted from bauxite by *electrolysis*.

Electrolysis is the name given to the process by which a direct electric current is passed through a solution between two electrodes:

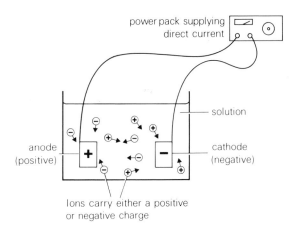

power pack supplying direct current

anode (positive)

solution

cathode (negative)

Ions carry either a positive or negative charge

During electrolysis the positive ions in solution are attracted to the negative electrode (the *cathode*) and the negative ions in solution are attracted to the positive electrode (the *anode*). When the ions reach the electrodes, they gain or lose an electron and change from ions to atoms.

Aluminium is obtained by these steps:

1. Extraction of bauxite from the surface deposits with huge earth-removing machinery.
2. The ore is crushed and heated, together with sodium hydroxide, under pressure.
3. Unwanted residues of iron oxide and other impurities are filtered off leaving *alumina* (aluminium oxide).
4. The alumina is dissolved in a molten mineral called *cryolite* in order to make it conduct electricity.
5. Electricity is passed through the molten mixture. The electric current deposits the aluminium and keeps the mixture hot:

Carbon anode which has to be lowered
as the oxygen released burns it away

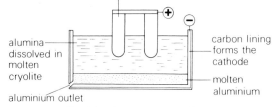

alumina dissolved in molten cryolite
aluminium outlet
carbon lining forms the cathode
molten aluminium

Aluminium ions carry a positive charge and move to the cathode.
Oxygen ions carry a negative charge and move to the anode

6. The carbon anode is lowered as it gets burnt away with the oxygen (which is released during electrolysis).
7. The pure molten aluminium is run off.

The process of obtaining aluminium from bauxite uses large amounts of energy, which makes aluminium more expensive than steel. Four tonnes of coal and 20 000 kilowatt hours of electricity are used during the production of one tonne of aluminium.

Task 2.3 Extraction of lead from lead oxide

1. Scoop out a hollow in the top of a block of carbon.

2. Place the carbon block in a clamp.
3. Place about 15 g of yellow lead oxide in the hollow.
4. Using a gas blowpipe heat the lead oxide continuously.
5. The oxygen combines with the carbon in the block to form carbon dioxide, leaving metallic lead in the hollow:

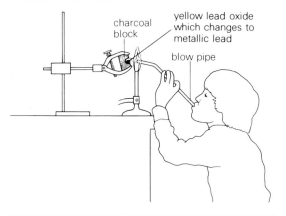

charcoal block
yellow lead oxide which changes to metallic lead
blow pipe

Questions: Rocks and minerals

1. Write single sentences to answer the following questions.
   (a) Why is lead added to petrol?
   (b) Which metamorphic rock is derived from limestone?
   (c) What is pig-iron?
   (d) Stainless steel is an alloy of three elements, what are they?
   (e) Aluminium is extracted from which ore?
   (f) What age are the oldest rocks on earth?
   (g) What age are the newest rocks on earth?

2. Describe the extraction and use of a non-metal under the following headings:
   (a) The work in the quarry.
   (b) Treatment of the quarried material.
   (c) Uses to which the final products are put.

3. Describe the extraction of a metal from its ore. Support your descriptions with diagrams and chemical equations.

4. What factors determine whether or not a metal is recycled? By reference to a single metal describe the advantages gained by recycling.

3 Water*

Water and life

Water is vital to life and accounts for over 60% of the weight of most plants and animals. The vast quantities of salt water in the oceans support algae and other plants which account for 60% of the world's photosynthesis (page 69); this photosynthesis is very important as it maintains a constant oxygen supply to the atmosphere. Water, both fresh and salt, provides an environment for countless millions of aquatic plants and animals and supplies man with an important protein rich food – fish.

Water is an essential constituent of soil and provides the means for nutrients to enter the plant and move around within it. Water is also the basis of the transport system within plants and animals and enables the removal of waste products from the body. It is used to remove dirt from our food and from ourselves and also to transport organic and other wastes from our homes.

---

*This chapter deals with the properties of water and its treatment for man's use. Other aspects of water appear in Chapter 4 page 44 and Chapter 9 page 114.

Water in home and field

Task 3.1

List the various uses of all the water that enters your home; during a single day record how much water is used and then divide the total consumption by the number of people in the home: this figure will give the average consumption per person.

The following figures may help you with the above task:

* A person needs an intake of between 1 and 2.5 litres per day.
* The average toilet cistern holds 9 litres.
* An average bath, one-third full, holds 120 litres.
* An average washbasin, half full, holds 4 litres.
* An automatic washing machine on normal cycle uses 150 litres.
* One-third the water used for a bath is enough for a shower.
* The national average household usage of water is over 200 litres per person per day.
* It takes 1350 litres of rain or irrigation water to produce food (vegetable) for one person for one day.

Would the production of meat take more or less water than the production of vegetables?   ...Q.1

Water in industry

In addition to domestic and agricultural use of water, industry requires vast amounts:

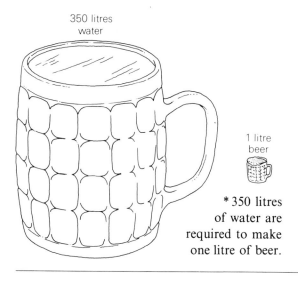

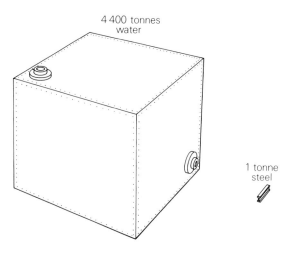

*350 litres of water are required to make one litre of beer.

*4400 tonnes of water are used in the production of 1 tonne of steel.
*It took over 80 litres of water to manufacture the paper in this book you are now reading.

Water for heating and cooling

Water is an excellent medium for transferring heat from one place to another – a fact man makes good use of in domestic heating:

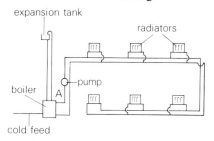

Is pipe A taking water to or from the boiler? ...Q.2

Water is also used for cooling:

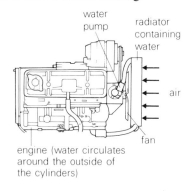

Task 3.2

Copy the last diagram and insert arrows to indicate the direction the water flows.

Describe how the system works, explaining the function of each part.

Water is used during the generation of electricity both to transfer heat and for cooling. The huge towers in the photograph above are just for cooling and are performing a function similar to that of a car radiator.

Constituents of water

The chemical formula for water is H_2O; this means that each molecule of water contains two atoms of hydrogen and one atom of oxygen.

Experiment 3.1

Water can be split into its two constituent elements (which are both gases) in the laboratory by electrolysis (page 23) as follows:

1. Three-quarters fill a trough with water and add a small quantity of sulphuric acid to help the water to conduct electricity. (**Caution:** always add the acid to water and not vice versa.)
2. Fill two burettes with a similar solution and support in the positions shown using two retort stands.
3. Place a platinum electrode in the base of each burette and connect to a 12-volt supply of direct electric current.

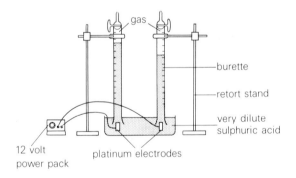

4. On the electrodes, bubbles form which rise and collect at the top of the burettes.
5. Continue until enough gas has collected to enable it to be tested.
6. Compare the volumes of gas in the two burettes. There should be twice as much gas in one burette as in the other; in practice however the gases partially dissolve in the water and the 2:1 ratio may not be exact.

Test the gas in each tube. Oxygen will relight a glowing wooden splint and hydrogen burns with a loud 'pop'.

Did hydrogen collect above the negative electrode or the positive electrode? ...**Q.3**

Which gas had the larger volume? ...**Q.4**

Note: sulphuric acid was added to make the water a better conductor. It is possible to show that the acid has remained unchanged during the experiment and that there is as much at the end as there was at the start.

Will the volume of water have increased, reduced or remained the same? ...**Q.5**

Water as a solvent

Water is a *solvent* in which many substances *dissolve*. The dissolved substance is called the *solute*.

Experiment 3.2

1. Take two 250 ml beakers and pour into each about 200 ml of water.
2. To one beaker add 25 g of dry finely powdered clay.
3. To the other beaker add 25 g of copper sulphate.
4. Stir the contents of each beaker vigorously.

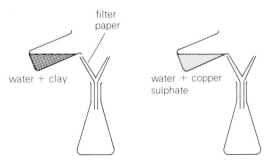

5. Pour each through a clean filter paper.
6. Examine both filter papers.

What do you see on each filter paper? ...**Q.6**

Experiment 3.3

1. Make a second suspension of clay and stand it in a cupboard alongside the beaker of copper sulphate solution.
2. Examine both beakers one week later.

What has happened? ...Q.7

When a substance dissolves in water it breaks up to give separate ions which become surrounded by water molecules. Ions move throughout the solvent.

$$CuSO_4 \rightarrow Cu^{2+} + SO_4^{2-}$$
(copper   (copper   (sulphate
   sulphate)   ion)   ion)

($2+$ in the equation above shows that two electrons have been lost from each atom of copper. $2-$ shows that two electrons have been gained by each sulphate radicle.)

Experiment 3.4

1. Pour about 25 ml of the copper sulphate solution into an evaporating dish.
2. Place the dish on a gauze and tripod.
3. Use a bunsen burner to gently boil off the water.

What remains in the dish? ...Q.8

The copper sulphate is now *anhydrous* (without water) and looks white; add a drop of water and it will turn blue. This is a useful method of testing whether a liquid is water: water turns anhydrous copper sulphate blue.

Experiment 3.5

To test the hypothesis that the amount of a substance which can be dissolved in water varies with temperature:

1. Put 100 ml of water into a 250 ml beaker.
2. Add sodium chloride (common salt) one gram at a time to the water; stir after adding each gram until the salt has dissolved.
3. Continue until no more salt will dissolve and a *little* salt lies on the bottom of the beaker. The water is now holding as much salt as possible and the solution is said to be *saturated*.
4. Place the beaker on a gauze and tripod and gently raise the temperature.
5. Stir and observe.

Does warm water hold more, less or the same amount of salt than an equal volume of cold water?
...Q.9

Water and Gas

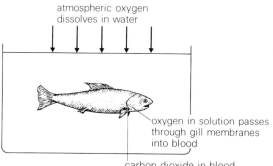

Not only solids dissolve in water; gases will too. Most water-dwelling creatures obtain their oxygen from the dissolved gas in the water.

Saturated solution

Water will hold only a certain amount of a solute in solution. This can be demonstrated by adding salt, a little at a time, to a beaker of water and stirring after each addition. At first the salt dissolves readily, but a point is reached where some salt remains on the bottom and no amount of stirring will dissolve it.

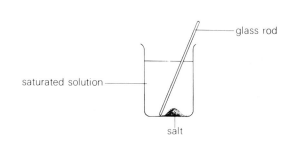

Experiment 3.6

Collect some pond (or river) water and devise an experiment to test whether warming the water raises or lowers the oxygen content.

In order to conduct this experiment you will need to test for oxygen, one method of doing this is described below:

The chemicals required are manganese (II) sulphate solution, which is prepared by mixing 100 g $MnSO_4$ (II) in 200 ml distilled water, and alkali–iodide solution, prepared by mixing 100 g sodium hydroxide and 30 g of potassium iodide in 200 ml distilled water.

Caution: sodium hydroxide can cause serious burns.

Fill a 250 ml stopper bottle brim full with the water which is to be tested for oxygen content.

Using a 2 ml syringe, add 2 ml of manganese (II) sulphate solution followed by 2 ml of alkali–iodide solution, making sure the syringe tips are below the surface of the water. Replace the stopper, making sure no air is trapped in the top, and shake. The teacher will then add 2 ml of concentrated sulphuric acid. Replace the stopper and shake; the solution will now be a clear yellow–brown. The depth of colour indicates the amount of oxygen which was in the water sample: a pale colour indicates low oxygen content, a deep colour indicates a high oxygen content.

Does warm water hold more or less oxygen than cold water? ... Q.10

Tap water

Tap water contains dissolved salts; in most areas the evidence for this can easily be seen on the inside of a well-used kettle, as some of the salts from the water are deposited inside and form a *scale*.

The impurities in water give it a distinctive taste. (Compare the taste of tap water with that of distilled water.) The impurities also supply some essential salts to the diet.

The fluorine content of drinking water affects dental health:

Fluorine content		*Effect on dental health*
Below	1 ppm	Dental decay may occur in some people.
Between	1 ppm and 15 ppm	Healthy teeth more likely in most people.
Above	15 ppm	Healthy teeth but mottled appearance in most people (*dental fluorosis*).

Healthy teeth

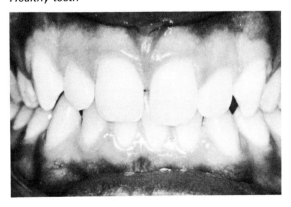

Decayed teeth

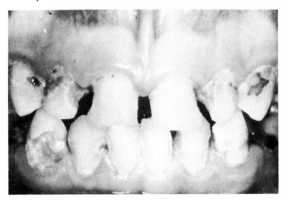

In some areas fluoride is added to water supplies to improve dental health. The maximum level permitted in drinking water is 15 parts per million.

Maximum permitted levels of other impurities are as follows:

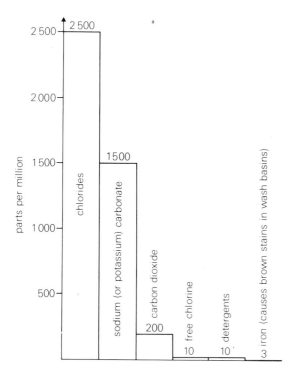

In addition, the possibility that 100 ml of water contains one disease carrying bacteria is considered unsafe.

Impurities can cause water to be *acid* or *alkaline*.

soils and rocks. Some of the salts contained in the soil and rocks will dissolve in the water. Common examples of salts dissolved in this way are calcium sulphate, magnesium sulphate, calcium chloride and magnesium chloride.

2. While in the air, rain dissolves small quantities of carbon dioxide forming a very weak solution of carbonic acid:

$$CO_2 \quad + \quad H_2O \quad \rightarrow \quad H_2CO_3$$
(carbon dioxide)   (water)   (carbonic acid)

As this weak acid flows over chalk or limestone rocks (or through soils to which lime has been added) the following reaction takes place:

$$CaCO_3 \quad + \quad H_2CO_3 \quad \rightarrow \quad Ca(HCO_3)_2$$

(calcium carbonate (chalk))   (carbonic acid)   (calcium hydrogen carbonate)

The action of the acid converts the insoluble calcium carbonate to soluble calcium hydrogen carbonate, which then dissolves in the water.

Water which contains dissolved calcium and magnesium salts is described as 'hard'. When soap is used in hard water, the chemicals in the soap first react with the calcium or magnesium salts to form a scum. It is not possible to produce a lather until the salts have all been used by the soap; hard water therefore wastes soap.

Investigation 3.1

Use a sensitive pH meter or universal indicator to test the tap water in your area; it may be acid, neutral or alkaline.

Acidity is due either to dissolved carbon dioxide or, if the water has originated from peaty lands, to organic acids. Alkalinity is due to dissolved calcium bicarbonate or other salts.

Sources of impurities in water

1. Before reaching the river, reservoir or well from which it is extracted, most water flows through

---

Investigation 3.2

To investigate the action of soap in different types of water

1. Obtain a number of samples of water from different sources, e.g. tap water, water from another area, boiled tap water, river water, rain water, distilled water.
2. Prepare a soap solution by mixing 200 ml of industrial methylated spirits with 200 ml distilled water and dissolving 4 g of sodium oleate in the mixture, add a further litre of distilled water.

3. Use a pipette to add 50 ml of the water to be tested into a conical flask.

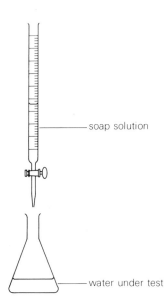

soap solution

water under test

4. Fill a burette with the prepared soap solution.
5. Add soap solution to the water, one ml at a time, and shake after each addition.

6. When a permanent lather has formed (i.e. one that lasts for 30 seconds) record how much soap has been used.
7. Repeat with the other samples of water.
8. Compare the amounts of soap required by different water samples to produce permanent lather.

If you live in a hard water area where the hardness is due to calcium hydrogen carbonate, the above investigation will show a marked difference between tap water and boiled tap water. The reason for this is that when water containing calcium hydrogen carbonate is boiled the following reaction takes place:

$$Ca(HCO_3)_2 \rightarrow CaCO_3 + CO_2 + H_2O$$
(calcium   (calcium   (carbon   (water)
hydrogen   carbonate)   dioxide)
carbonate)

As calcium carbonate is insoluble it leaves the water as a precipitate. This type of hardness is called *temporary*.

Water softening

Permanent hardness

Not all hard water can be changed by boiling. Hardness which cannot be removed by boiling is called *permanent hardness*. It is caused by the presence of calcium and magnesium salts other than the hydrogen carbonate (e.g. chlorides and sulphates).

Ion exchange

Permanently hard water can be softened by passing it over an ion-exchange resin which is rich in sodium ions, as in a commercial water softener. As the water passes over the resin the calcium (or magnesium) ions change places with the sodium ions. The sodium ions enter the water and the calcium (or magnesium) ions remain in the resin. Sodium salts present in water do not prevent soap from forming a lather.

The sodium ions in the resin will eventually be used up; when this happens the resin can be restored by passing a solution of sodium chloride (NaCl; common salt) through it.

A model of a water softener can be made by purchasing some ion-exchange resin and using it as shown:

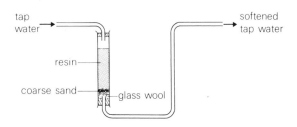

tap water →   softened tap water

resin

coarse sand

glass wool

Why does hard water need to be softened? ...**Q.11**
Does the scale inside a kettle come from permanent or temporary hard water? ...**Q.12**

Physical properties of water

Specific capacity

Water holds more heat than almost any other substance; it takes 4.2 joules* to raise one gram of water through one degree Celsius.

How many joules will be required to raise the temperature of one gram of water at 10 °C to 20 °C?
...**Q.13**

How many joules will be required to raise the temperature of 20 g of water at 8 °C to 16 °C? ...**Q.14**

The amount of heat energy required to raise the temperature of one gram of a substance through one degree Celsius is called its *specific capacity*.

The specific capacity of water is 4.2 joules per gram (J/g). Specific capacity of other substances:

	J/g
copper	0.38
alcohol	2.31
mercury	0.14

Water has a high specific capacity, which means that water holds more heat than almost any other substance.

---

*A joule is a unit of *energy* and is the amount of work done when a *force* of one newton moves through a *distance* of one metre. A *newton* is a unit of force and is defined as the force that acting for one second on a mass of one kilogram gives it a velocity of one metre per second.

Melting point

The temperature at which pure ice melts is called 0 °C. If the ice contains salt then its melting point is lowered; this fact is made use of by many local authorities, which spread salt (often mixed with grit) on icy roads to make them safe for traffic.

High pressure will also reduce the melting point of ice. This can be demonstrated by hanging two weights on a wire stretched across a block of ice. The ice under the wire melts and as the wire sinks the water above refreezes as the pressure is removed.

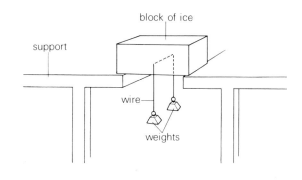

Boiling point

The temperature at which water boils is called 100 °C as long as the pressure of the air above it is normal (760 mm of mercury at sea level).

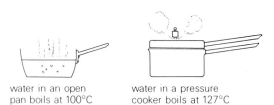

water in an open
pan boils at 100°C

water in a pressure
cooker boils at 127°C

Increasing the air pressure raises the boiling point of a liquid.

Reducing the air pressure lowers the boiling point, thus water at the top of a mountain will boil at a lower temperature than water at the bottom. The difference in the boiling points will depend upon how high the mountain is.

Why can't you make a good cup of tea above 1000 m?
...**Q.15**

Density

Density of water (g/ml) at different temperatures:

°C	0	2	4	6	8	10	12	14	16	100
Density	0.9998	0.9999	1.0000	0.9999	0.9998	0.9997	0.9995	0.9992	0.9989	0.9584

At what temperature does water reach its maximum density?   ...Q.16

Heating causes most substances to expand and cooling causes them to contract. This is true of water at temperatures over 4 °C but as the temperature falls below this level water stops contracting and begins to expand.

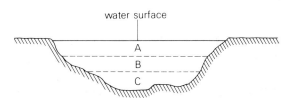

The layers in the pond water above represent water at three different temperatures, 0 °C, 2 °C and 4 °C. Which layer is which?   ...Q.17

Ice is less dense than cold water; this is of very great importance for pond life, as it causes ponds to freeze from the surface downwards and not from the bottom upwards.

In summer, when all the water in the pond or lake is above 4 °C, it is the coldest water which is the most dense and therefore sinks to the bottom.

In deep lakes and reservoirs where there is not enough turbulence caused by currents or wind to mix the layers, the top can become very much warmer than the bottom.

As all the sun's energy is absorbed by the top few metres of water, there is no energy source to warm the deeper layers and they remain cold.

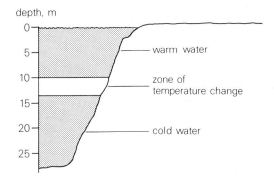

Vertical section through a pond

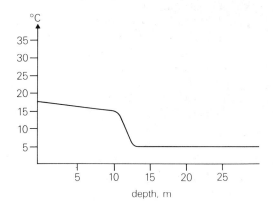

Water temperatures in a deep lake in summer

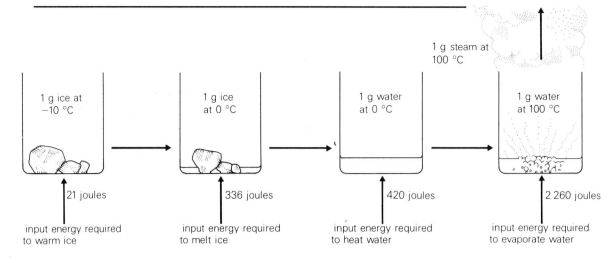

1 g ice at −10 °C	1 g ice at 0 °C	1 g water at 0 °C	1 g water at 100 °C
21 joules	336 joules	420 joules	2 260 joules
input energy required to warm ice	input energy required to melt ice	input energy required to heat water	input energy required to evaporate water

1 g steam at 100 °C

Energy involved in changing 1 gram of ice at −10°C to 1 gram of steam at 100°C

What is the total amount of energy involved to turn 1 g ice at −10 °C to steam? ...Q.18

(*Note:* 10 g would require 10 times as much energy at each stage, 34 g would require 34 times, and so on.)

Latent heat of vaporisation

When a pan of cold water is placed over a flame the energy of the flame raises the temperature of the water. When boiling point is reached the temperature remains constant, as the energy of the flame is being used to change water into steam. The energy required to convert water into steam (2260 joules per gram) is called the *latent heat of vaporisation*. When water evaporates at low temperatures it still requires the latent heat of vaporisation to change it from a liquid to a gas.

To demonstrate this, wet your thumb and blow on it. You can feel the evaporating water taking heat from your thumb, making it cold.

Will transpiring leaves be warmer or colder than the surrounding air? ...Q.19

When water vapour becomes liquid it releases the latent heat of vaporisation. The reason why steam can give such a nasty burn is due to the latent heat of vaporisation.

Latent heat of fusion

There is also a latent heat associated with the change of state from liquid to solid. Ice at 0 °C requires 336 joules per gram to turn it into water at 0 °C; similarly, water at 0 °C releases 336 joules per gram as it becomes ice. The heat associated with melting and freezing is called the *latent heat of fusion*.

Some potato growers make use of this in late spring when radiation frosts are expected which would damage potato foliage: the plants are sprayed with cold water during the night and the water freezes on the leaves and releases the latent heat of fusion, preventing the temperature from falling below 0 °C. As potato foliage is not damaged until a temperature of −1 °C is reached the crop is saved. Fruit blossom is often protected in the same way:

Note: any movement or any change of state of matter (solid, liquid or gas) always involves the transfer of energy.

The world's water

Seventy-one per cent of the earth's surface is covered with water or ice, the total volume of which is 1.37 billion cubic kilometres. However, 99% of this water is high in dissolved salts – salt water – and is of little direct use to man, as he requires fresh water. The world's water passes through a *hydrological cycle* and at any one time about one per cent of the total is in this cycle and is free from dissolved salts – i.e. it is *fresh*. It is this fresh water which man taps for his own use.

The hydrological cycle

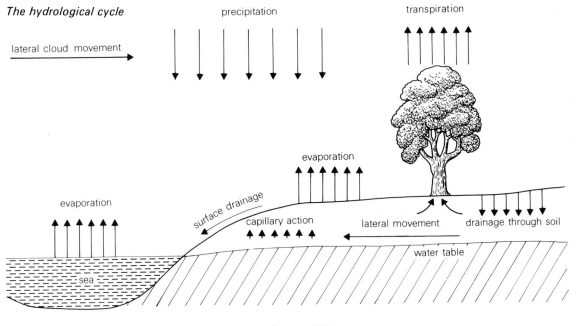

What energy source drives the hydrological cycle? ...Q.20

Task 3.3

Make a list of all the places in the world where the water is either free or almost free from dissolved salts.

Your list no doubt includes porous rocks. Some rocks do not hold water and are said to be *impervious*. Porous rocks, however, can hold large quantities of water. A rock which is holding water is called an *aquifer*:

Examine the diagram opposite and answer the following questions:

Is the top of the artesian well higher or lower than the water table? ...Q.21

(If it is lower then water will flow without being pumped.)

Does rain falling on area B recharge the aquifer? ...Q.22

Vertical section through an aquifer

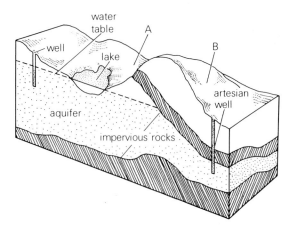

What volume of water could be pumped from the wells without affecting the level of the lake? ...Q.23

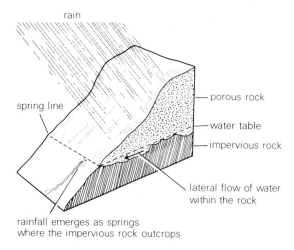

rain

spring line

porous rock

water table

impervious rock

lateral flow of water within the rock

rainfall emerges as springs where the impervious rock outcrops

Task 3.4

Fill a glass jar with dry, coarse sand, pour in some water, and watch what happens. The water seeps down between the particles and displaces the air until it finds its level. You now have the lower layer filled with water and an upper layer of damp sand; this is a model of an aquifer – the bottom of the jar represents a layer of impervious rock and the water level in the sand represents the water table.

Water supply

Water is extracted for man's use from aquifers, rivers, lakes and reservoirs but before it is pumped into the mains supply it has to be *treated* to make it safe to drink. The treatment water receives depends upon which impurities are present.

Methods of treating water:

1. Screening

Screens (sieves) allow water to flow and catch debris. The spaces or holes in the screens are large at the point of extraction, where the screen consists of vertical bars 20 mm in diameter and 75 mm apart. Further from the point of extraction, the screens gradually become finer until they are so fine that no algae can pass through.

2. Sedimentation

Moving water picks up and carries particles; the faster the flow the larger the particles which are carried. When the water stops the particles are dropped as sediment; thus in theory if water is stored in large shallow tanks all sediment will fall to the bottom and clean water can be run off from the top. In practice *sedimentation tanks* do not work as well as the theory suggests; some particles in the water are very small and fall very slowly, and water flowing in and out of the tanks causes turbulance which disturbs the sediment, making it rise.

Certain substances can be added to make sedimentation a more efficient method of purification – two such substances are lime (calcium hydroxide) and alum (aluminium sulphate).

If lime or alum is added to water in which small particles are suspended then the particles join to form a *floc*; this sinks much more rapidly than individual particles. This process is known as *flocculation* and is commonly used in the treatment of water (see page 27).

3. Upward-flow sedimentation

Another type of tank which removes sediment is the *upward-flow sedimentation tank*:

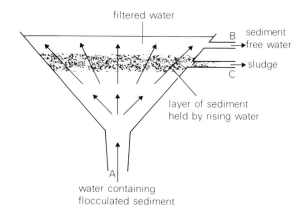

filtered water

B sediment free water

sludge

C

layer of sediment held by rising water

A

water containing flocculated sediment

Water which has been treated with lime or alum is pumped in at A. The shape of the tank causes the upward velocity of the water to fall rapidly until a point is reached where the upward velocity of the water is equal to the velocity at which the sediment is falling. This causes the sediment to remain in the same spot and a layer of sediment forms across the middle of the tank. Rising water passing through this layer is filtered and loses its sediment. Clean water is drawn from near the surface and the sludge can be removed through pipe C as necessary.

4. *Filtering with sand beds*

Much of our water supply is filtered through a bed of sand and gravel. Sand beds are not simple

Vertical section of a sand filter bed

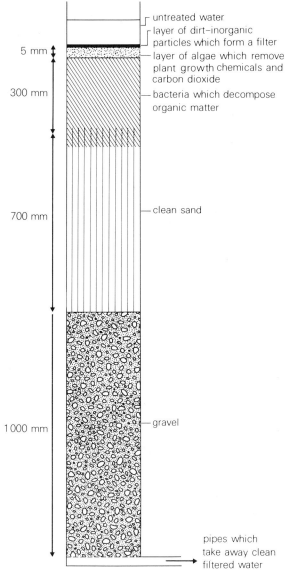

filters; they clean the water in three ways, physically, chemically and biologically.

When water passes through a sand bed the following occur:

(a) The water is filtered through a very thin layer of dirt.
(b) It is stripped of nitrates, phosphates and carbon dioxide by algae.
(c) The oxygen produced by the algae reacts with some impurities, making them harmless.
(d) The water is stripped of organic matter by the action of bacteria.
(e) It is left with simple inorganic substances in solution.

Which layer cleans by (a) a physical method?
(b) a chemical method?
(c) a biological method?
...Q.24

As the layer of dirt builds up on the surface, the rate of flow is maintained by increasing the depth of the water on top (this, of course, increases the pressure). About every three months the layer of dirt, together with the top 50 mm of sand, is removed and a fesh layer of sand is added.

5. *Sterilisation*

After filtration the water is sterilised, either with chlorine or with ozone. Chlorine is the cheapest and therefore the most common method of sterilisation. Liquified chlorine gas is injected into the water at a carefully calculated rate. The chlorine takes about half an hour to kill the bacteria and any chlorine left after this is removed by adding sulphur dioxide.

Task 3.5

Explain each of the stages A, B, C, D and E in the water treatment plant shown in the diagram over the page.

After treatment, water is piped into the water *mains*, from which pipes lead to the places where it will be used.

Water treatment plant

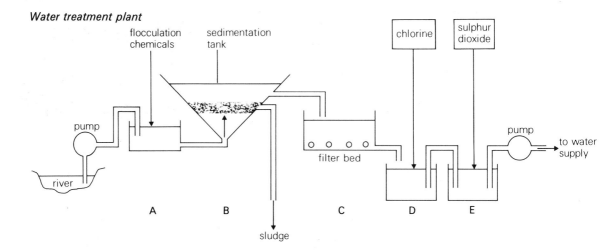

Sewage and its treatment

After being used water flows down drains and other disposal systems into the sewers as *sewage*.

Sewage is the liquid waste from a community and is a mixture of organic and mineral matter. This matter is in several forms:

1. Light material floating on the surface.
2. Particles of solids in suspension.
3. Substances in solution.
4. Living organisms of bacteria, viruses and protozoa.

By law, all water containing sewage must be treated before being discharged into ponds, lakes, or watercourses. There is no law yet to prevent untreated sewage from being dumped in the sea.

In the UK there are over 5000 sewage works where the sewage is treated and the water content recycled for possible future use.

Water on its journey to the sea in rivers is often used more than once; the *effluent* of one town becomes the *supply* of the next. Water is naturally cleansed while it is in the river by the action of oxygen and by living organisms. Sewage is screened as it enters the sewage works to remove large solid matter. It then lies in sedimentation tanks where 80% of the solid matter settles out as sediment.

Depending upon the type of plant, one of the two following processes is adopted:

1. The water from the settling tanks is pumped to a filter bed where rotary sprinklers deposit it on the surface of gravel beds. The gravel in these beds is coated with millions of invertebrates, algae and bacteria which remove the organic matter which is still suspended in the water. The water is then held in a final settling tank before being discharged into a river as effluent. A sewage works of this type is called a *trickling filter* sewage works.

2. The water from the settling tank is pumped into a further tank where it is mixed with sludge from the final settling tanks and stirred rapidly; this oxygenates the mixture and allows the organisms in the sludge to break down the organic

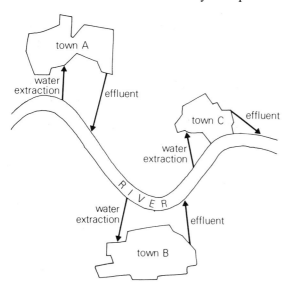

matter. The activated sludge is passed to a final settling tank where the remaining solids settle. Effluent is drawn from the top of this tank and discharged into the river. Some of the sludge in the final settling tank is used to innoculate sewage in the activated slurry tanks with bacteria and other organisms; the remainder is dried and used as fuel. This type of sewage works is known as an *activated sludge* sewage works.

Rotary sprinklers

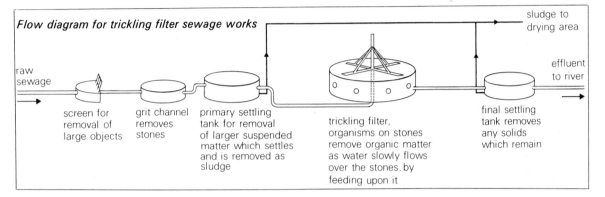

Flow diagram for trickling filter sewage works

sludge to drying area

effluent to river

raw sewage

screen for removal of large objects

grit channel removes stones

primary settling tank for removal of larger suspended matter which settles and is removed as sludge

trickling filter, organisms on stones remove organic matter as water slowly flows over the stones, by feeding upon it

final settling tank removes any solids which remain

Task 3.6

Draw a flow diagram of an activated sludge sewage works. (Remember, sludge from the final settling tank is used in two ways.)

Investigation 3.3

Obtain three samples of river water: one just upstream and one just downstream from the local sewage works effluent pipe, the third sample from one kilometre downstream.

Perform the following tests on each sample and compare:

1. *Suspended solids*. Shake the water, pour 250 ml into a measuring cylinder and filter. Open out the three filter papers and make a visual comparison.

2. *Oxygen content*. Use the oxygen test described on page 29 to compare the level of dissolved oxygen in each sample.

3. *Detergents* (cleaning agents which do not contain soap). Pour 250 ml into a one litre measuring cylinder and shake ten times. Use a stopwatch to time how long the bubbles persist on the surface.

4. *Nitrogen*. Add 4 ml of Nessler's reagent to 100 ml of a water sample. If nitrogen (in the form of ammonia) is present then the water will yellow. The deeper the colour the more nitrogen is present.

5. *Smell*. Leave 250 ml corked in a 500 ml flask for 24 hours; smell as you remove the cork.

Put your results in a table like this and discuss your conclusions:

Sample collection point	Suspended solids	Oxygen content	Detergents	Nitrogen	Smell
Above effluent					
Below effluent					
1 km downstream					

Dam wall

Water storage

Water has to be stored to even out the effects of intermittent rainfall; in addition, during times of drought there is insufficient water in our aquifers, lakes and rivers to meet our needs. The seven water authorities who manage the water supply have the responsibility of maintaining a constant supply. The most common method of storing water is by *reservoir*; a reservoir is an artificial lake created by placing a dam across a river.

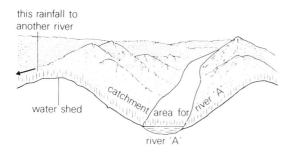

Once the reservoir has filled, water can be piped from it to other parts of the country. The volume of a reservoir is reduced by gradual silting up and measures have to be taken to prevent this. (Tree planting in the catchment area is very effective.)

The building of a dam and the flooding of the valley behind is usually opposed by local populations for many different reasons; some will lose their homes and farms as they disappear under the new lake, some will object to areas of countryside with which they are familiar being turned into a lake, while others will dislike the intrusion and noise of large lorries and earth-moving machines. Woodlands and favourite paths may be lost and the environment of the entire area will undergo a very big change, including the loss of many habitats for local flora and fauna. The path of migratory fish will be blocked, preventing them from returning to their spawning grounds (a few dams have bypasses to allow fish to swim through; these are often only partly successful). On the other hand, opportunities may be created for fishing and sailing and habitats formed for different species of birds and other creatures. As well as for water supply, dams are also constructed for hydro-electric power schemes (page 89).

Hydro-electric dam

Task 3.7

List all the effects you can think of which the construction of a dam and reservoir will have upon the human community and the animal and plant life in the immediate areas. Put these effects into two columns, one headed 'Detrimental' and the other 'Beneficial'.

Desalination

In some areas rainfall is insufficient to meet the needs of the population; one such area is the island of Jersey where the summer population is trebled by the influx of tourists. Here additional water can be obtained from a *desalination plant* which converts salt sea water into fresh water:

Investigation 3.4

To find the amount of salt in sea water:

1. Weigh an evaporating basin.
2. Take 100 ml of sea water and completely evaporate it, a little at a time, from the basin.

Desalination plant in Jersey

3. Weigh the evaporating basin with the salt inside. **How much salt do you find?** ...**Q.25**

4. Multiply the increase in weight by ten to express the result in grams per litre.

Salt content in water

Fresh water	Brackish water	Sea water
Concentration of salts too low to be detected by taste	Low salt content but high enough to be detected by taste	High salt content, average 35 g/litre

Methods of desalination:

1. *Electrodialysis.* In this type of plant the ions in solution are attracted to electrodes through filters which prevent their return.

This leaves partially desalinated water between the filters which can be pumped out for further treatment.

Electrodialysis is used in some parts of the world to treat brackish water but it is too expensive to treat seawater in this way as it uses very large amounts of electric current.

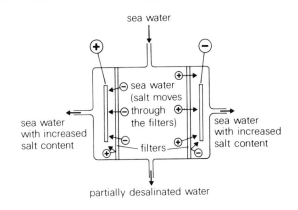

2. *Distillation.* Sea water is distilled easily in the laboratory using the apparatus illustrated below. In practice, however, the plant that desalinates water by this principle is very complex; 'waste' heat from the condensers is used to warm the sea water as it enters the system. The pressure above

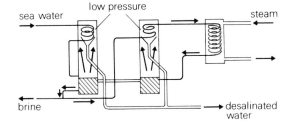

the sea water is lowered to reduce the boiling point of the sea water.

With the exception of the solar still which utilises the sun's energy in areas of exceptional sunshine, all desalination plants require a very high energy input. Water obtained by desalination is very much more expensive than natural fresh water supplies.

Remember: water is a very precious commodity which must never be wasted.

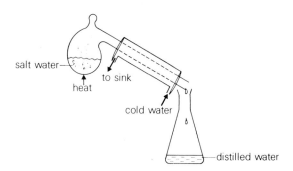

Questions: Water

1. Write single sentences to answer the following questions.
   (a) How many litres of water are used in the production of one litre of beer?
   (b) Compared with other substances, does water have a high or a low thermal capacity?
   (c) For what reason do some Water Authorities add flouride to the water supply?
   (d) What effect does carbon dioxide have upon the pH of the water in which it is dissolved?
   (e) What is the volume of one gram of water at one degree Celsius?
   (f) Some rocks are described as aquifers, what does this mean?
   (g) For what reasons are dams constructed in this country?
   (h) Why is desalination an expensive method of obtaining fresh water?

2. How does the effluent from a sewage works differ from raw sewage? Describe the processes which have brought about these changes.

3. A water supply may be *'soft'*, *'temporarily hard'* or *'permanently hard'*.

   (a) Explain the italicised terms in the statement above. Where possible support your explanation with a chemical equation.
   (b) Describe a method of removing permanent hardness from water.
   (c) In what ways is the removal of hardness beneficial?

4. The most important service to a city is a constant supply of safe, fresh water. By reference to an area you have studied show how this is achieved.

5. As water at 0 °C freezes it releases 336 joules of energy per gram.
   (a) By reference to the molecular structure of water, explain how the liquid retains this energy (see page 83).
   (b) Describe one way in which man makes use of the heat released by freezing water.

6. (a) Distinguish between a renewable and a non-renewable resource.
   (b) With reference to a particular example say why it is necessary to conserve a *renewable* resource and show how this can be achieved.

4 The biosphere

Food chains

How food chains work

A food chain shows how the sun's energy is used by the natural world before it is all 'lost' as heat.

1. Light energy arrives from the sun, some of which falls on green plants.
2. The plant traps a small proportion (1%) of this energy and converts it to chemical energy by *photosynthesis* (see page 70). The chemicals which contain the energy form the plant's tissues.
3. The animal eats the plant and breaks down the plant tissue in its digestive system, releasing the energy for its own use.
4. Most of the energy will be lost as heat while the animal performs its normal activities. (This energy is not actually lost; it is dissipated as heat.)
5. A little of the original energy will still exist as chemical energy in the animal's tissues.
6. A second animal may eat the first and use the energy stored in its tissues; by this time almost all of the original energy trapped by the plant has been used up. This happens in all food chains:

Trophic levels

The energy levels in a food chain are called *trophic levels*, from the Greek word for food – *trophe*.

Trophic level I – grass

The green leaves of the grass trap parts of the sun's light energy during photosynthesis and lock it up in the plant tissue. As the grass plant respires, it uses over half of the energy it has locked away; this energy moves fluids around the plant and grows roots, flowers and seeds. The energy used by the grass becomes heat and is lost to the surroundings.

Trophic level II – rabbit

In order to obtain energy the rabbit eats a lot of grass; the energy it gains is used up in the following ways:

1. Keeping the animal warm.
2. Moving about, digging holes, finding food and so on.

Only a small proportion of the energy the rabbit gained from the grass is passed on to the fox

grass grows ⟶ rabbit eats grass ⟶ fox eats rabbit

trophic level 1   **trophic level 2**   **trophic level 3**

3. Growing bones, hair and muscles.
4. During normal body functions, e.g. digestion, breathing, heart beating.
5. Producing a new generation.
6. Some energy is lost in faeces and urine.

Used energy is lost to the surroundings as heat; only a small proportion of the energy the rabbit gained from the grass is available for the fox.

Trophic level III – fox

The fox obtains all its energy from that stored in the rabbit's tissues and organs.

The fox requires energy for the same reasons as the rabbit; there is almost none of the original energy left so he needs to eat a lot of rabbits and the fox is the end of the chain. When the fox dies, however, the small amount of energy remaining will be utilised and released by the organisms of decay, invertebrates, fungi and bacteria.

Loss of energy

At each trophic level as much as 95% of the energy may be used and lost.

Energy of trophic level I: 400 joules
Energy of trophic level II: 20 joules
Energy of trophic level III: 1 joule

With such large losses of energy along a food chain it is easy to see why they are generally short and why there are less foxes than rabbits. The fox must have a large territory in order to catch enough rabbits – the foxes are thus so thinly spread that no animal could live by eating only foxes.

At which trophic level is the weasel in the following food chains?
(a) leaves: millipedes: shrews: weasel?
(b) seeds: voles: weasel?   ...Q.1

Pyramid of numbers

Numbers usually decrease along a food chain, as in the case of grass: rabbits: fox.

The pyramid of numbers does not *always* work. What about the following food chain?

  apple tree: winter moth larvae: thrush

Here there is only one tree but many winter moth larvae; the pyramid of numbers will be top heavy:

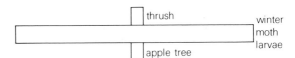

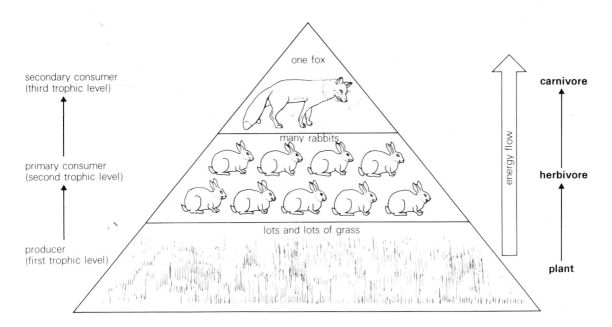

If instead of numbers the biomass (the total weights of the organisms) is used the pyramid is restored:

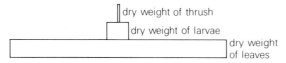

Food webs

A food chain is only a small part of the way different organisms interact and are dependent upon each other: rabbits eat plants other than grass, foxes eat food other than rabbits, and other creatures eat the rabbit:

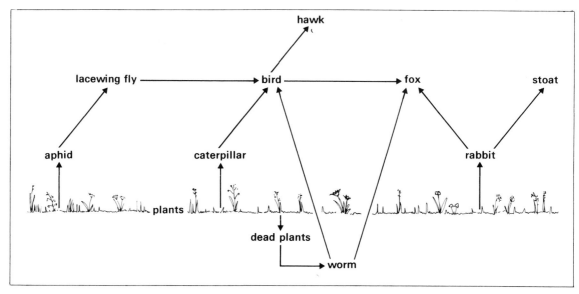

This is a *food web*, and, like life itself, begins to get very complicated.

Task 4.1

Arrange the following in a food web:
  plants, earthworms, millipedes, centipedes, shrew, voles, stoat, rabbit, buzzard, fox (voles, millipedes and rabbits are herbivores) hedgehog.

Man is also a part of many food chains:

If the wheat in each of the food chains A and B contains 1000 joules of energy, how much energy is available to man in chain A? How much energy is available to man in chain B? (Assume a loss of energy of 90% at each trophic level.) ...Q.2

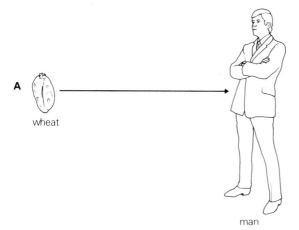

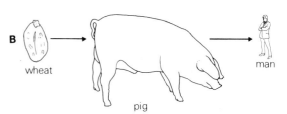

Plant succession

Areas of land upon which there is no vegetation (e.g. new areas of blown sand, areas exposed by a receding water line from a lake edge, and disused industrial sites) do not remain bare but become colonised with plants. Even areas of bare concrete turns green as plants invade. Plants growing on concrete will be quite different in kind from the plants growing in areas where deeper rooting is possible.

Over a long period of time (if left alone by man) a bare area will usually become a forest. It takes a long time before a forest is established and during this time the flora is subject to drastic but gradual change; this change is called *plant succession*:

first colonisers → grasses and herbaceous plants → shrubs → small quick-growing trees → large trees

Coltsfoot – a first coloniser

On derelict industrial sites, coltsfoot is often one of the first plants to appear. It has deep rhizomes and tough leaves and its seeds are wind-borne. Groundsel, greater knapweed and thistle (and others with wind-borne seeds) soon follow. These plants hold the surface and prevent it from eroding; they trap blown soil and leaves which add nutrients and help the ground to retain water. In this improved surface and sheltered by the first colonisers, seeds of other species germinate and grow.

The plants now begin to compete with each other for water, nutrients and light; light is a most important factor and taller plants have a considerable advantage, shading the lower plants, which often die out.

Species of grass are usually seen fairly early in the succession; grass seeds are light and easily blown, germinate quickly and establish a dense root system near to the surface. Grass is green throughout the year, and can make use of light on warm days when other plants are dormant. Another factor which favours grass is its ability to withstand being grazed; buds and growing regions of most plants are held high and will be removed by browsing animals but the buds and growing regions of grass are low and are often left undamaged by feeding animals when they bite off the top of the plant.

As the numbers of species of plants increase, a variety of foods are produced and animals and birds will begin to visit, bringing with them seeds of yet more plants, shrubs such as bramble, gorse, broom and hazel. These species and many more begin to appear and, being taller than most herbaceous plants, begin to dominate the vegetation. Which actual species survive depends upon many environmental factors, the most important of which is the soil. As shrubs appear some shaded herbs will die out:

Different stages of plant succession can be seen along the banks of the old railway cutting

In turn the shrubs become overshadowed by trees; it is then the turn of some shrubs to die, leaving the trees to dominate the area. This is illustrated over the page.

Climax vegetation

The type of tree which finally dominates depends upon the climate and soil type; it may be Scots pine, beech, oak, ash, alder or even birch. More often than not, UK woodlands contain mixed species of trees, the actual species depending upon local conditions; for example on clay soils the main species may be oak with alders in the wetter parts, while on sandy soils the main species may be Scots pine and birch. Calcareous soils (i.e. soils rich in calcium) favour ash.

The final vegetation in the succession will regenerate itself; as the older trees die out they will be replaced by younger ones of the same species. This final vegetation is called the *climax vegetation*. The climax vegetation gives a greater primary production than any other type of natural vegetative cover.

Examples of primary production:

Vegetation	Primary production (g/m^2 per year)
Forest	1300
Fresh water	1200
Hazel/bramble	700
Grassland	600
Open ocean	125

As plant succession continues, the total organic matter increases; also increasing with time is the number of ecological niches (see page 51), which in turn increases the number of different animal species.

Climax vegetation

Seres

Examples of areas where succession is occurring are called *seres*. Thus a *hydrosere* is an area of vegetation which was once water. A *lithosere* is an area of plants colonising bare rock, and a *xerosere* is one which is arising under dry conditions.

Deflected succession

The natural succession is sometimes diverted by an external factor, by the change of a watercourse or by animals; for example if rabbits enter an area before the shrubs become established they may eat all the young shrubs and trees before they have a chance to grow above the herbaceous plants; while the rabbits remain there will be no trees. This is referred to as *deflected succession*. In addition, the burrowing of the rabbits will disturb and bury many of the herbaceous plants; as these begin to regrow the rabbits will eat off the shoots and the area may become covered with nettles as rabbits do not eat nettles.

What type of vegetation would you expect in an area where a flock of sheep was introduced before the shrubs became established during a natural succession? ...Q.3

Investigation 4.1

Locate a number of areas where plant succession is taking place and record the plants which are growing. Notice how slight changes in the micro-environment determine the species which are growing; a concrete patch may be covered with moss except where a crack allows enough soil to support a small flowering plant like grass or groundsel. Note how the presence of animals changes the vegetation: for example the track in the photograph is an area of grass through ribwort – this is caused by a goose which walks along this track a number of times each day. The ribwort cannot withstand being trampled on by the goose, and the grass cannot compete successfully with the ribwort as the goose grazes it as soon as it is large enough to bite.

The areas you locate do not have to be large, if possible study the areas over a period of time and record any changes.

Goose track

Dominance and codominance

A species is often referred to as *dominant*. A dominant species is not the most numerous – it is the one which has the most effect, thus in an oak woodland the dominant species will be oaks. Where a small area is being considered a single beech tree may be dominant as it shades a large area with its spreading branches and dense leaf mosaic.

If two trees are of similar size they are said to be *codominant*:

Woodland ecology

The ecologist considers the forest in separate layers as shown in the figure opposite.

Occasionally there is a fourth layer of moss under the field layer – the *ground layer*. Sometimes a whole layer may be absent; for example, under closed-canopy beech trees the tree layer may be the only layer represented, as the dense canopy cuts out light and the surface rooting habit of the species keeps the surface soil dry.

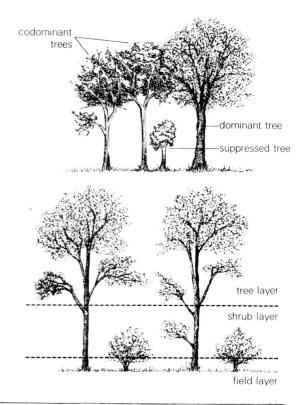

Layers in typical woodlands

The field layer may vary throughout the seasons as some field layer flora, which cannot tolerate too much shade, have evolved a fairly short photosynthetic period and make use of the spring sunlight before the trees are in leaf:

Soil type	Tree layer (dominant species)	Shrub layer	Field layer
loam	beech	bramble (sometimes absent)	wood sorrel dog's mercury hairy violet
calcarious, well drained	ash	dogwood hazel hawthorn spindle privet	early flowering herbaceous perennials
clay	oak	alder sallows	sedge
dry loam	oak	often absent elder bramble	bracken bluebells foxgloves
acid sand	oak	birch	heath bedstraw

Photosynthetic periods of some woodland plants

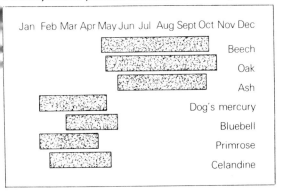

The environment of the woodland, together with all its plants and animals and the way in which they interact with each other, is known as the *ecosystem*. You are now studying a woodland ecosystem; there are other ecosystems, e.g. a pond ecosystem.

The animals of the woodland

The trees and plants with leaves, stems, flowers, fruits, seeds and roots provide a lot of food for the animal world. Each food source represents a biological *niche*; there is always a species of animal to feed on each niche. One reason why a woodland ecosystem (a community of organisms plus their environment) can support a very wide range of animal species is that they occupy different niches and are not competing for food (e.g. both aphid and leaf miner feed on leaves; as the former sucks the sap and the latter eats the tissue they are not directly competing).

Task 4.2

Make an enlarged copy of the chart below and in the blank boxes enter the names of animals which occupy that niche from the list overleaf.

Row A: primary consumers.
Row B: secondary consumers.
Row C: top carnivores.

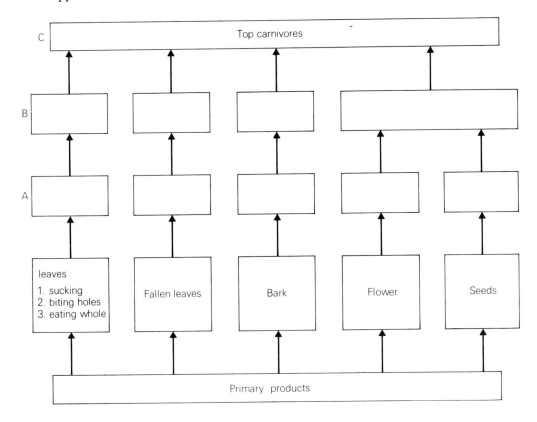

Chart of primary consumers

Niche	Animal
Leaves	deer, caterpillars, leaf miners, voles, frog hoppers (cuckoo spit)
Fallen leaves	worms, springtails, woodlice, mites, millipedes
Bark	woodlice, millipedes, grey squirrel, rabbits
Flowers	butterflies, moths, bees, flies
Fruits and seeds	weevils, caterpillars, woodmice, voles, nuthatch, chaffinch, thrush, badger
Fungus	snails, slugs, fly larvae

Chart of secondary consumers

Niche	Secondary consumer
Aphid	hoverfly, ladybirds, lacewing larvae
Voles	owl, fox, stoat
Earthworms	mole, badger, blackbird, fox
Millipedes Woodlice	centipedes, shrew, tits, hedgehog
Caterpillars	robins, tits
Springtails Mites	beetles, harvestmen, centipedes, beetle larvae
Rabbits	badger, fox (take only young or sick ones), buzzard, stoat
Butterflies	tits

Chart of tertiary (third) consumers

Niche	Tertiary consumer
Ladybirds Lacewings	tits, warblers
Blackbird	sparrowhawk, owl
Hedgehog	fox
Shrew	fox, badger, hedgehog, weasel
Beetles	blackbird, thrush

Another food source is the dung of animals which is consumed both by flies and their larvae and by dung beetles. Dead animals (carrion) are consumed by a large variety of animals including the carnivores, magpies and crows.

The deer has no predator since the wolf became extinct in this country.

The pine marten is the only effective predator of the squirrel; these are now very rare, due partly to persecution by gamekeepers.

Woodlands as dormitories

Woodlands are used by animals and birds as dormitories. Wood pigeon, starlings and crows, for example, roost and nest in the wood but spend much of their feeding time in surrounding countryside.

Task 4.3 Read the following account and answer the questions opposite.

'A mature oak woodland contained only trees which were over 200 years old. In an attempt to discover why the wood was failing to regenerate itself a group of scientists designed the following experiment: Sixty sites, each half a metre square, were taken at random throughout the wood and were cleared of vegetation exposing the bare soil. Ten acorns were placed on each site and twenty sites were covered with cages of 50 mm mesh, twenty were covered with cages of 5 mm mesh and twenty were left uncovered. The cages were pressed into the soil to prevent burrowing underneath. The germination and growth of the acorns was recorded for a period of two years.'

1. Suggest an hypothesis which this experiment was designed to test.
2. What fact should be known about the acorns before the experiment took place?
3. Why were two different mesh sizes used?
4. What was a possible cause of no regeneration if all the acorns disappeared except for the ones in the 5 mm mesh cages which began to grow?
5. What was a possible cause of no regeneration if all the caged acorns grew and the uncovered ones disappeared?
6. What was a possible cause of no regeneration if all the acorns grew?
7. What was a possible cause of no regeneration if only the caged acorns grew but the seedling trees disappeared when the cages were removed?

Project 4.1

Woodland

The best way to understand an ecosystem is to make a practical study, as follows:
1. Obtain a large-scale map of a woodland area to which you have access. Note the roads, footpaths and land use of the wood and its surrounding area. Note also the contours, particularly the slopes, in relation to the cardinal points and any streams or other bodies of water.
2. Select an area of the woodland for study. The actual area of woodland studied will depend upon the number of students and the time available. Make an accurate map of this area by the following method:

Apparatus: large tape measure, ball of string, some bamboo poles.

Method:
(a) Select a base line AB, drive in a pole at each end and stretch the string tightly between the poles:

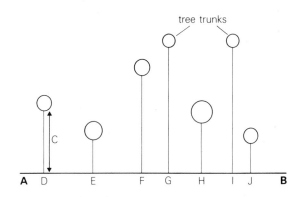

(b) Measure the distance AB.
(c) Measure the *shortest* distance from each tree to the base line; record also the distance from A to the points D, E, F ... etc.
(d) Back in the laboratory, transfer the distances you have recorded directly on to graph paper to form an accurate map. Mark in the cardinal points, also if possible *the direction of the prevailing* wind. Record on your map the species of each tree.

3. Make records of precipitation and other weather conditions:

Apparatus: maximum and minimum thermometers, rain gauges, hand anemometers, wet and dry bulb thermometers, light meter.

Method:

(a) At heights of 1 metre record the maximum and minimum temperatures inside and outside the wood over as long a period as is practical (take all readings in shade).

(b) Set up rain gauges inside and outside the wood. Inside the wood, set gauges at measured distances from the bole of a dominant tree, starting near to the tree and finishing in open canopy. Record rainfall daily once again over as long a period as possible – not less than say, two weeks.

(c) Measure the windspeeds in the wood at various heights. If two anemometers are available simultaneously, record the windspeed inside and outside the wood at a height of $1\frac{1}{2}$ metres.

(d) Using wet and dry bulb thermometers and the chart below, compare the relative humidity inside and outside the wood.

Another useful method to compare humidity is to fit a potometer (see *Rural Science 3*) with a porous pot instead of a leafy shoot.

(e) Use a light meter to record light.

Compare the different environmental conditions by making a copy of the chart below and completing it:

Relative humidity for use with wet and dry thermometer

Depression of wet bulb	Dry bulb temperature (°C)															
	0	2	4	6	8	10	12	14	16	18	20	22	24	26	28	30
1	81	84	85	86	87	88	89	90	90	91	91	92	92	92	93	93
2	64	68	71	73	75	77	78	79	81	82	83	83	84	85	85	86
3	46	52	57	60	63	66	68	70	71	73	74	76	77	78	78	79
4	29	37	43	48	51	55	58	60	63	65	66	68	69	71	72	73
5	13	22	29	35	40	44	48	51	54	57	59	61	62	64	65	67
6		7	16	24	29	34	39	42	46	49	51	54	56	58	59	61

	Inside the wood		Outside the wood
	Closed canopy	Open canopy	
Maximum temperature			
Minimum temperature			
Temperature range			
Rainfall (mm)			
Wind speed ground level			
2 m high			
6 m high			
10 m high			
Humidity			
Trees in leaf			
Trees dormant			
Light			

What difference would you expect to find inside and outside a wood? ...Q.4

4. *Soil study*

   Apparatus: soil auger, pH meter, polythene sample bags, tie-on labels.

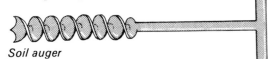

Soil auger

Method:

(a) Collect soil samples from a number of random points and mix. Use the key on page 67 to determine the soil type.

(b) Take soil samples from areas where the vegetation differs, put each sample in a polythene bag. Record where each sample was collected on a tie-on label. Use the tie to seal the bag. If you put the label inside the bag it may become wet and difficult to read.

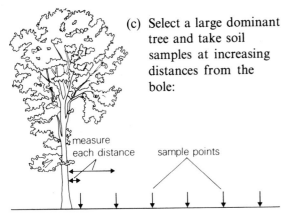

(c) Select a large dominant tree and take soil samples at increasing distances from the bole:

measure each distance   sample points

Record each distance on the sample label. For each sample take the pH and answer the questions, 'Does the pH of the soil differ with increasing distance from a tree?' and (using also other students results) 'What effect does the soil pH have upon the type of vegetation?'

5. *Line transect* (do when most plants are in flower):

   Apparatus: flora, string, poles, tape measure, spirit level.

   Method:

   (a) Use a flora to identify any plants you do not know in the field and shrub layers. Do not pick the plants.

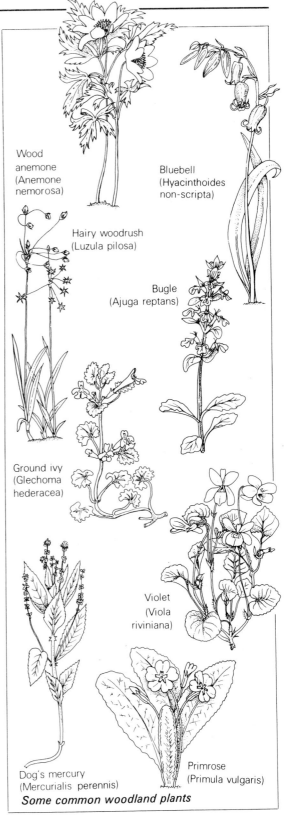

Wood anemone (Anemone nemorosa)

Bluebell (Hyacinthoides non-scripta)

Hairy woodrush (Luzula pilosa)

Bugle (Ajuga reptans)

Ground ivy (Glechoma hederacea)

Violet (Viola riviniana)

Dog's mercury (Mercurialis perennis)

Primrose (Primula vulgaris)

Some common woodland plants

Once you are familiar with the plants make a line transect.

(b) Select an area where there is a variety of vegetation, e.g. the edge of a wood from deep shade to full sunlight.

(c) Stretch a line across this area at a height of 1.5 metres between two trees or, if there are no convenient trees, between two poles erected for the purpose. Use a spirit level to check the line is level:

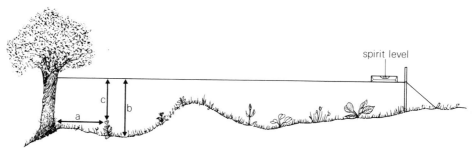

(d) Move along the line measuring distances a, b, c for each species and record on a chart like this:

Distance from tree a	Height of line b	Plant species	Height of plant b − c	Condition of plant
2 m 4 m	1.5 m 2.1 m	bare ground bluebell	— 170 mm	flowering

What measurements would you take if a plant was higher than the line?   ... Q.5

(e) Use the information on the chart to make a scale drawing on graph paper.
Classify the plants on the DAFOR scale, referring to the area in which you are working, i.e. Dominant, Abundant, Frequent, Occasional, Rare.

---

6. *The animals*
   Apparatus: pooter, Barlese funnel, stick for beating, white sheet 2 m square, plastic cups, raw potato, damp sacking, sweep net, bucket of of water, specimen jars.
   Methods
   A. Animals in the litter and soil

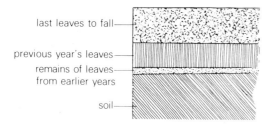

Vertical section through a woodland floor

(a) Collect 10 litres of litter, making sure all layers are represented in the sample. Tip the little on a white sheet and carefully search for animals. Place the animals in different specimen jars according to species; small specimens are collected in a pooter:

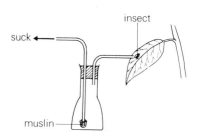

(b) Collect a sample of soil and crumble it in a bucket of water; many of the soil animals will float to the surface and can be collected.

(c) Use jam jars or plastic cups to make pitfall traps, making sure the traps are protected from birds and rain by covering with large leaves, e.g. cabbage. Beetles and other active insects may fall into these.

(d) Put pieces of raw potato under damp sacking. 24 hours later collect any animals found there (usually millipedes and slugs).

(e) Animals can be extracted from both soil and leaf litter by means of a Barlese funnel, as they go deeper to escape light and dehydration they fall through the gauze and are collected in the tube below.

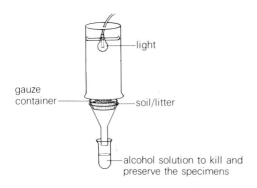

B. Animals feeding or nesting on plants

(a) Make a careful search of tree leaves, twigs, bark and branches for any animals you can find. Even when invertebrates are abundant this method often produces very disappointing results, a much larger yield is obtained by beating:

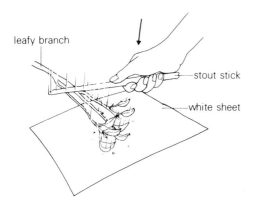

(b) Two people stretch a sheet underneath the end of a leafy branch and a third person gives the branch two or three sharp taps with a stout stick; this will dislodge insects and their larvae which are caught on the sheet below. This method of collection need not be confined to leafy shoots, flowering and fruiting branches will often produce large numbers.

When beating a tree would you expect to find more aphids or ladybirds? ... Q.6

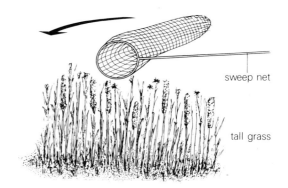

(c) To collect invertebrates in tall vegetation, a sweep net is moved rapidly across the surface of the vegetation, disturbing it and dislodging some of the invertebrates which get caught in the net. When comparing two areas by this method an equal number of strokes of equal length should be made.

Larger animals

Vertebrates are much more difficult to find and sample; they are either nocturnal or run away and hide as man approaches. Bird-watching from a hide is almost impossible with a large group of people in a short time, although some birds and their nests will be seen upon most occasions when a visit is made. If an owl's perch can be located owl pellets can be collected from the floor; after soaking for 24 hours the pellets can be teased apart and the various bones, feathers and hair can be examined to reveal something of the owl's diet. Although hidden, the mammals leave evidence of their presence which must be carefully looked for or it will be missed by the untrained eye.

Rabbit

If rabbits are numerous, as they may be if the wood borders farmland, they may be seen hopping away when you first approach, their white tails bobbing; this is often preceded by drumming the ground with the hind feet to warn other rabbits of approaching danger. In open grass rabbit tracks are distinctive as rabbits always put their feet down in the same spot as they bound along.

These tracks may lead to a well trodden hole in a hedge or clump of brambles. Rabbits often sit on mounds and their spherical black droppings can be seen in large numbers on these mounds. Unlike many other vertebrate droppings these are used by very few invertebrates as a food source, since having passed through the rabbit's gut twice they have very little energy left in them.

Rabbit burrows are often found in groups; these are interconnected to form a warren. The flora around a warren is usually very different from the flora elsewhere in the wood, because of soil disturbance, trampling and feeding.

Fox

The entrance to a fox earth is larger than most rabbit holes and there is less likelihood that rabbit droppings will be found, although some may be present. Evidence of recent meals (bones, feathers etc.) may be seen in the vicinity of the entrance, especially in May and June when cubs are being nursed. The hole may also have a strong smell of fox, which is an obnoxious stale smell.

Badger

Badger sets are larger still and can be identified by careful searching of nearby trees for evidence of claw marks made by stretching badgers after they emerge in the evening. The footprint of the badger is very distinctive – look for the impression of the claws 6–10 mm in front of the pad marks. Rolls of grass also indicate the hole may be that of a badger; these have been left when the animals have been collecting fresh bedding material.

Squirrel

In most woodlands (except in remote parts and where all the trees are conifers) the only squirrels present will be grey ones. Although the grey squirrel is tame in some parks, in natural woodlands it is not inclined to show itself. Its presence can be detected by its winter drey which is on a branch near where it joins the trunk, or by its summer drey which is smaller and situated much further from the trunk on a twiggy branch. Dreys can be confused with the nests of crows and magpies; the presence of leaves on the twigs indicates a drey rather than a nest, for birds use dead twigs while the squirrel will break off leafy twigs for building material. Although the leaves on these twigs will die they will not drop off as there is no abcission layer. Other indicators of grey squirrels are claw marks made on tree bark as they climb, fir cones dismembered to obtain seeds (care here: the crossbill damages fir cones in a similar way) and small scratch marks in the ground where acorns have been either buried or retrieved. Young hardwood trees stripped of large areas of bark above the height of two metres in early summer will almost certainly be the work of the grey squirrel.

Stoat and Weasel

These animals use the burrows of others and are very difficult for the amateur to detect, even when they are quite numerous. A dead rabbit with a bloody neck is probably the work of a stoat, and a pair of very noisy excited birds at nesting time could indicate that a weasel has found its nest and they are trying to frighten it away.

The voles, woodmouse, yellowneck mouse and shrews can be sampled with the aid of Longworth live traps (*Rural Science 1*, p. 63) but use of these traps is restricted to members of the Mammal Society (1982 Wildlife and Countryside Act).

Mole

Moles are often present in established woodlands and you are aware of them by the hills their tunnelling produces. The mole is a solitary creature and a group of a dozen or more hills may be the work of only one mole.

Stoat (*Mustela erminea*)

Weight	♀ 140g	♂ 210g

European shrew (*Sorex araneus*)

weight 7 g

65 mm   30 mm

When your investigations are complete:

1. List all the food sources produced by the trees and plants.

2. List all the primary consumers, making sure that all the niches are filled.

3. Make a list of all possible food chains, using all the animals whose presence you have detected.

4. Fit the food chains into a food web to cover the whole woodland. Draw arrows in the direction of the energy flow. The energy used at each trophic level will be lost as heat until none of the original sun's energy is left – except that which is retained in the trees as increase in timber; even this will be released in years to come when fungus and beetles break down the dead trees or someone enjoys a log fire.

Project 4.2
A fresh water pond

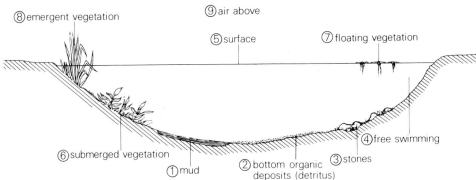

⑧ emergent vegetation   ⑨ air above   ⑤ surface   ⑦ floating vegetation   ④ free swimming   ⑥ submerged vegetation   ① mud   ② bottom organic deposits (detritus)   ③ stones

A fresh water pond produces nine habitat zones. These are numbered in the diagram above.

Visit a fresh water pond (or other body of fresh water, e.g. lake, canal, river); if the area is large (i.e. more than one hectare) a map can be made by making an enlarged copy of an Ordnance Survey map. If the area is small (i.e. less than one hectare) use the method described for the woodland study on page 53, measuring the points on either side of the water from the base line.

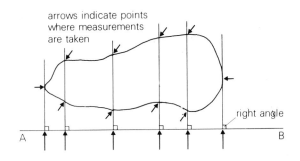

arrows indicate points where measurements are taken

right angle

A   B

Map produced by a group of boys and girls following a day's field study

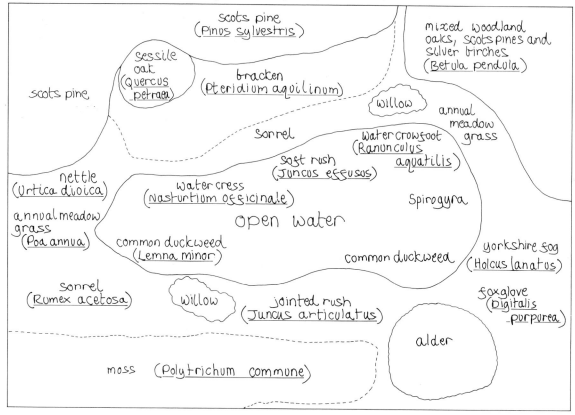

Transfer your measurements directly to graph paper and draw in the outline of the pond.

Identify and record the vegetation immediately around the water.

Record also areas overhung by trees.

Take the temperature of the water near the surface, and on the bottom; compare these temperatures with the air temperature above the surface.

Will the day–night temperature range be larger, smaller or the same in the water as on the bank?
... **Q.7**

Use a key to identify the plants growing in the water and transfer this information to the map.

Examples of pond plants are shown opposite. Draw a diagram to show the zones where your plants were growing.

The animals

Apparatus: pond net, sweep net, white dishes, polythene sheet, plankton net, keys, pooter.

Different methods are used to sample the animals in the various zones:

(a) The animals on the surface can be seen by careful observation. These should be observed and their presence recorded before the water is disturbed.

(b) The air above can be sampled by using a sweep net and transferring the animals by means of a pooter, in a way similar to that used in the woodland.

(c) Plankton may be concentrated into a jar by means of a plankton net:

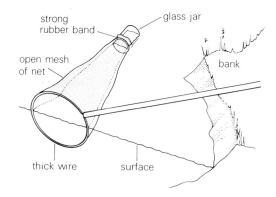

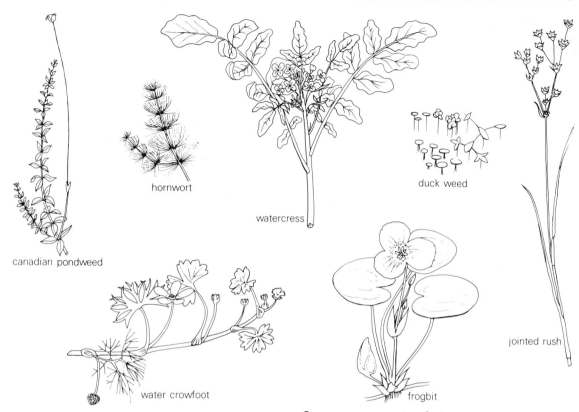

canadian pondweed

hornwort

watercress

duck weed

jointed rush

water crowfoot

frogbit

Some common water plants

(This net may be used only on large ponds. If your pond is small use a glass jar and let water settle in it. Take it back to school and, in the warm classroom, plankton will multiply rapidly.)

Sweep the net across the surface of the water, making sure the mouth does not become completely submerged. Make a sweep of about 5 m; remove the jar and retain for laboratory study. In the laboratory put a drop on to a slide, cover with a coverslip and examine under the microscope; the plankton may be seen to be a mixture of microscopic plants and animals, although they are difficult to distinguish. Leave the jar in a warm, light window for a few days (it will probably begin to smell as the scum of an algal bloom forms on the surface).

What is the most likely cause of this algal bloom?
... **Q.8**

Make a microscopic examination of the scum.
(d) Half fill a white dish with pond water. Take the pond net and lower it into the water in an area where there are no plants:

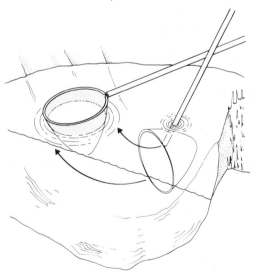

Collecting animals from the surface layer of a pond

Make a three-metre sweep as rapidly as possible and bring the catch out of the water. Transfer any animals in the net to the water in the dish.

Observe each animal carefully, identify it with a key, and record in your field notebook.

Collecting animals living on submerged vegetation

When all the animals have been recorded and given a letter from the DAFOR scale (page 56),

lower the dish into the water and allow them to escape.

(e) Repeat (d) above, except this time sample the animals living on and among the submerged vegetation. To do this place the pond net among the plants, beat them gently to dislodge any animals and then bring it smartly out of the water.

(f) Refill the white dish with water and place it on the plastic sheet. Push the net into the mud on the bottom of the pond and scoop up a sample. Empty the net into the centre of the plastic sheet and search through the mud placing any animals you find into the white dish. Identify and record as above before returning the catch and mud to the pond.

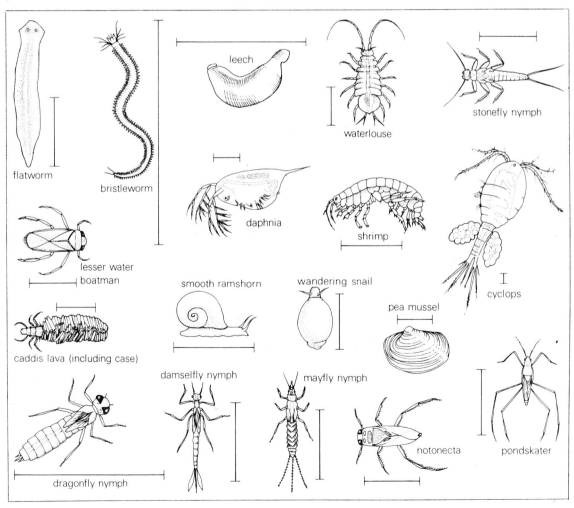

Thoroughly clean all the apparatus before returning to school.

Here is a selection of the animals you may catch:

The sun's energy which reaches the pond is used in various ways:

1. Some is reflected from the surface of the water.
2. Some enters the water and is absorbed as it passes through, warming the water.
3. Some is used by algae and other plants as they photosynthesise.

This last energy enters the food chain and is lost as heat at each trophic level until none remains.

Follow the energy flow through the ecosystem by arranging all the plants and animals you found in a food web. If there are deciduous trees nearby, do not forget to include leaves which blow into the pond and add to the detritus on the pond bottom.

Try to determine what effects man's activities are having upon this habitat; e.g. do any farm ditches empty into it, or do students rob it of animals? (The great diving beetle was once made extinct in Hertfordshire ponds due to the actions of schools.)

What substances may farm ditches contain which could cause changes in the ecosystem?   ... Q.9

Use the information below to determine the degree of pollution in your pond:

Stonefly and Mayfly nymphs will only be present in unpolluted water. Caddis fly larvae and fresh water shrimps can withstand some pollution. Water louse, midge larvae and leeches can survive in polluted water, but only sludge worm and rat-tailed maggot can survive in badly polluted water with a very low oxygen content ($< 4\text{cm}^3$/litre water at $5°$ C)

Questions: The biosphere

1. Write single sentences to answer the following questions.
   (a) How does browsing differ from grazing?
   (b) What vegetation is most likely to be found underneath mature, closed canopy beech trees?
   (c) Which animal is an effective predator of the squirrel?
   (d) What instrument is used to measure humidity?
   (e) What does each letter represent in the DAFOR scale?
   (f) What differences are there between the winter and summer dreys of the squirrel?
   (g) What is a pooter?
   (h) What effect did investigation by school children have upon the population of the great diving beetle in Hertfordshire?

2. (a) What is an ecosystem?
   (b) By reference to a specific ecosystem describe how energy flows through a natural environment.
   (c) What is the ultimate end of all the energy which enters an ecosystem?

3. From a habitat you have studied explain how a qualitative analysis was made of the fauna.

4. The following are important variable factors in an ecosystem:
   (a) temperature range
   (b) wind
   (c) humidity
   (d) rainfall
   What instruments are used to measure each of these factors and how are they used?

5. By reference to a specific ecosystem explain:
   (a) the difference between a food chain and a food web.
   (b) a pyramid of numbers and a pyramid of mass.

6. (a) For which resources do plants compete with each other?
   (b) By reference to this competition explain the various stages of plant succession from bare earth to climax vegetation.
   (c) Describe the parallel changes which take place with the associated fauna during this succession.

5 Food

We must have a regular supply of food for the following reasons:

1. To provide energy:
   (a) to keep warm;
   (b) to maintain body functions;
   (c) for work;
   (d) for recreation.
2. To provide the materials to build new tissues for growth and to replace those which are wearing out.
3. To supply vitamins which are necessary to maintain health.
4. To supply mineral elements, required by the body, to manufacture certain essential molecules.

Carbohydrates

Most of the energy requirements come from sugar, starch, fat and oil. Sugar and starch are carbohydrates and contain carbon combined with the elements from a number of water molecules, e.g. glucose ($C_6H_{12}O_6$), which is grape sugar, and sucrose ($C_{12}H_{22}O_{11}$), which is cane sugar.

Most of the carbohydrates in our food are derived from plants. Cereals, potatoes and sugar contain a high proportion of carbohydrate.

Task 5.1

Draw a histogram to show the percentage of carbohydrates in the following common foods: honey 76%, maize 85%, milk 4%, porridge oats 70%, grapefruit 12%, potatoes 20%, rice 80%, white bread 52%.

Oils and fats

Oils and fats are chemically similar (oil has a lower melting point than fat). They contain carbon, hydrogen and oxygen, but the proportion of oxygen is much less than it is in a carbohydrate. Some fats have the maximum amount of hydrogen the carbon can hold – these are called *saturated*; others have less hydrogen and are called *unsaturated*. Animal fats are usually saturated and plant fats are usually unsaturated. It is possible to combine extra hydrogen with unsaturated fat and saturate it; in this way margarine can be made from oil.

At which trophic level is man if he eats (a) butter? (b) margarine? ... Q.1

Protein

The food essential for body building is *protein*, which contains carbon, hydrogen, oxygen and nitrogen. A protein molecule is a chain of different substances called *amino acids*; there are 23 amino acids, 8 of which must be included in the diet if health is to be maintained. Animal products are rich in some essential amino acids, while cereals are rich in others. To obtain amino acids in the correct proportions, meals should contain food from both plant and animal origin, e.g. bread and cheese, fish and chips, egg on toast.

A pregnant woman requires more protein than one who is not pregnant. Why is this? ... Q.2

Protein-rich foods include milk, eggs, cheese, fish, meat and legumes. What have the first five foods in common? ... Q.3

Food (100 g)	Water (g)	Protein (g)	Fat (g)	Carbo-hydrate (g)	Calcium (mg)	Iron (mg)
Potatoes	78	1.4	trace	19.7	4.3	0.5
Beef	66	19	14	0	5.5	4.5
Eggs	74	12	12	trace	56	2.5
Fish (white)	80	18.7	0.5	0	41	0.5
Cheese	37	25	34	0	810	0.6
Peanuts	4.5	31	49	8	61	2
Cabbage	90	3.3	trace	3	75	9
Peas	80	6	trace	10	15	2
Wholemeal flour	15	9	2	73	35	3
Cornflakes	8	6	0.8	88	7	3
Butter	14	0.4	85	trace	15	trace

Daily requirements of protein vary according to age; a growing child requires three grams of protein per one kilogram of bodyweight each day, while an adult requires only one gram of protein per kilogram of body weight each day.

Vitamins

Vitamins are complex molecules required by the body in very small quantities to maintain health and prevent disease. A shortage of vitamin A can cause blindness; cod liver oil, liver, carrots and spinach are all rich in this vitamin. A deficiency of vitamin C affects teeth, bones and muscles; blackcurrants, orange juice and brussels sprouts are rich in vitamin C.

Other materials

Several inorganic elements play a vital role in our bodies; for example, our bones contain a high proportion of calcium and phosphorus, and each molecule of haemoglobin in our blood contains an atom of iron. Foods containing these elements, and several more, must be included in the diet.

Soil

The basis of nearly all food production is soil. Plant life is supported by a thin layer of this crumbly material. A soil which will support a crop is *fertile*; it consists of tiny fragments of rock which are wet with a dilute solution of salts. In between the rock particles are air-filled spaces and binding them together is organic material in the final stages of bacterial decay, called *humus*.

Re-read the last two sentences and then write down the six constituents of soil. Turn to the end of the book and check your answer. **... Q.4**

Soil types

Not all soils are the same. They vary in type from area to area – some are light and drain freely, others are heavy and tend to become waterlogged. Which crops can be grown depends not only upon climate but also upon soil type. The size of the rock particles which form the skeleton of a soil determines the type.

Soils formed from particles of diameters in excess of 0.2 mm are sands and soils formed from particles of diameter 0.002 mm and less are clays.

Differences between sand and clay soils:

Sand

free draining
warms and cools quickly
organic matter decays quickly
holds very little water
low in mineral salts
easy to cultivate
high air content
a 'light' soil

Clay

slow to drain
warms and cools slowly
organic matter decays slowly
holds a lot of water
high mineral reserves
difficult to cultivate
low air content
a 'heavy' soil

Pure sand or clay soils are very rare; most soils contain a mixture of different-sized particles and as a result have properties in between those of sand and clay:

100% sand	75/25	50/50	25/75	100% clay
sand soil	**sand loam**	**loam**	**clay loam**	**clay soil**

This chart discounts the medium-sized particles known as *silt*; when these are included it adds a third variable and the diagram becomes a triangle:

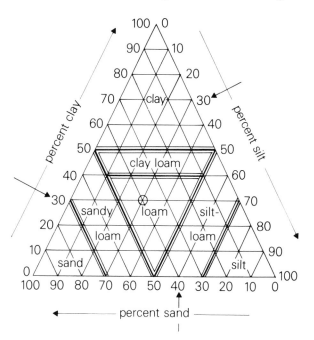

A soil with 30% clay and 40% sand will have a 30% (i.e. 100−70) silt content. These three quantities are arrowed in the triangle above; the point in the triangle which is directly connected to these three arrows is circled and shows the soil to be a loam.

Use the triangular diagram to determine the type of soil which has 60% silt, 20% clay and 20% sand.

Investigation 5.1

It is possible to estimate the type of soil by manipulating a wet ball of it with the fingers. Use the key opposite to determine the type of soil around your school.

Take about a heaped teaspoonful of soil which contains sufficient water and manipulate it to a state of maximum stickiness and plasticity, working out all the lumps. Then apply the following tests. *Note*: the soil *must* be sufficiently wet and extra water may need to be added at intervals.

Water and air

The size of the rock particles largely determines the water capacity of the soil, the smaller the particles the larger the surface area for a given volume of soil. Water is held in a thin layer on the surface of the particles – the more surface the more water.

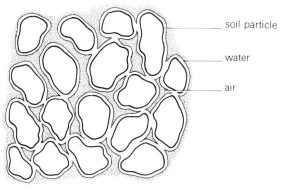

soil particle

water

air

(the water around a soil particle is continuous with the water around surrounding particles; if some water is lost from around one particle, water will flow from around neighbouring particles to replace it, leaving all of the layers a little thinner)

Key for estimating soil type

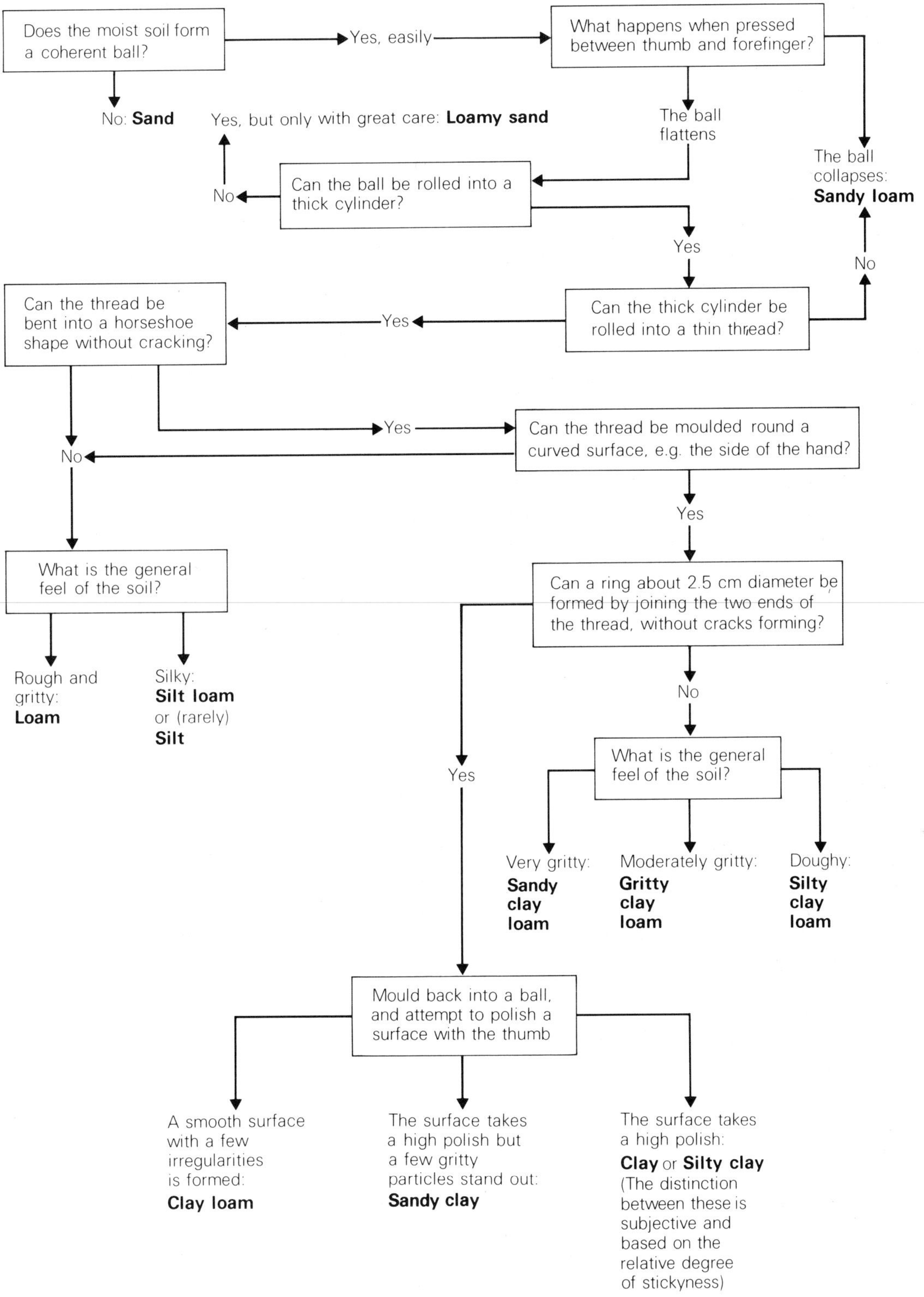

Does the moist soil form a coherent ball?

→ Yes, easily →

What happens when pressed between thumb and forefinger?

No: **Sand**

Yes, but only with great care: **Loamy sand**

The ball flattens

The ball collapses: **Sandy loam**

Can the ball be rolled into a thick cylinder?

No ←

↑ No

Yes

Can the thread be bent into a horseshoe shape without cracking?

← Yes ←

Can the thick cylinder be rolled into a thin thread?

↑ No

→ Yes →

Can the thread be moulded round a curved surface, e.g. the side of the hand?

No ←

Yes

What is the general feel of the soil?

Can a ring about 2.5 cm diameter be formed by joining the two ends of the thread, without cracks forming?

Rough and gritty: **Loam**

Silky: **Silt loam** or (rarely) **Silt**

Yes

No

What is the general feel of the soil?

Very gritty: **Sandy clay loam**

Moderately gritty: **Gritty clay loam**

Doughy: **Silty clay loam**

Mould back into a ball, and attempt to polish a surface with the thumb

A smooth surface with a few irregularities is formed: **Clay loam**

The surface takes a high polish but a few gritty particles stand out: **Sandy clay**

The surface takes a high polish: **Clay** or **Silty clay** (The distinction between these is subjective and based on the relative degree of stickyness)

The particle size also has an effect upon the air content of a soil; large particles do not pack as closely together as small particles, leaving much larger spaces to fill with air. (Comparing sand particles with clay particles is rather like comparing whole rice grains with ground rice.)

Humus

The humus content of a soil is of extreme importance; it is formed from plant and animal material as it decays. Humus is a black mass of complex chemical compounds which provides the soil water with a continual stream of inorganic salts. Plants absorb these salts and use them to build their tissues:

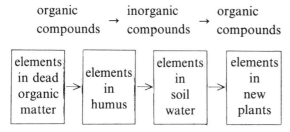

Humus is the vital link which passes the materials of one generation to the generations which follow.

Humus and soil structure

In addition, humus binds soil particles together and helps to prevent the erosion (washing or blowing away) of the soil from the underlying rock by wind, water and gravity. The binding of soil particles gives the soil 'structure'; soil will not run through the fingers like the sand at the seaside, rather it sticks together in lumps. Good fertile soils have a high humus content and a very crumbly structure, while poor soils have a low humus content with less and smaller crumbs.

Under grassland and trees the activities of earthworms and other organisms improve the crumb structure of soil as its humus content increases; when grassland is ploughed the humus content falls rapidly. On a mixed farm (i.e. crops and livestock) humus-forming materials in the form of manure are constantly added to the soil to replace this loss. On arable farms if soils are cropped with cereals every year then the humus level may become so low that the soil is destroyed and may become eroded. In most areas, to prevent erosion, 'break' crops are grown every few years; a 'break' crop is a non-cereal crop, often (but not always) a legume.

Feeding mankind

There are four methods by which our food can be obtained, although some of these are now history as very few people in the world now obtain their food by methods 1 and 2.

Method 1: hunting and gathering

Man does not disturb the soil; he lives on wild fruits, seeds, stems, leaves, bird's eggs, honey and captured animals.

Method 2: nomadic farming

Man cultivates a small area of cleared forest for a few years; when the fertility of the soil falls he abandons the area to nature and clears a new area. The abandoned area will return to forest and will be cleared again sometime in the future.

Method 3: subsistence farming

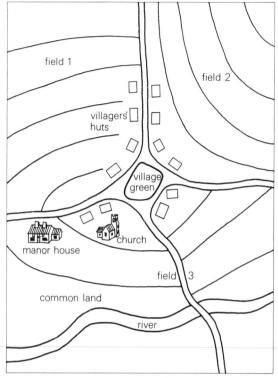

Man produces only enough food for himself and his family, there is no surplus to support an urban population. The area of cultivated land available to the village (or tribe) is divided into three fields, each family has one strip of land in each field. The fertility of the soil is maintained by 'resting' one of the fields each year. An area of common land is used for cattle, pigs, sheep and hens to add the necessary protein to the diet. This is one method of subsistence farming; there are many more using two, four or more fields; another example is the peasant farming system in the East.

Method 4: food production

The modern farmer produces enough food for his family and sixty other people who are not engaged in agriculture. Soil fertility is maintained by inputs of fertilisers (manufactured largely from fossil fuels). The whole operation depends upon machinery powered by fossil fuels which are provided by persons not engaged in agriculture.

By which of the four methods is your food supplied?
... **Q.5**

What food can still be obtained by Method 1?
... **Q.6**

With Method 1, man is part of the natural eco-system, living the life of an omnivore rather like the badger does today. The number of people would be small and the food supply would limit the population of man just as it limits the population of badgers or indeed any other wild animal.

The other three methods involve man adapting the ecosystem to suit himself and increase his own numbers; this will of course have a very big effect on all the other living things in the system. Once man cultivates and attempts to grow the species of his own choice, any 'wild' plant which competes with his crop becomes a 'weed' and any animal which attempts to eat his crop becomes a 'pest'. As man begins to crop the soil, he upsets the ecological balance; this has many effects, two of which are:

1. The soil becomes deficient in certain mineral salts which are essential for plant growth.
2. Certain organisms are favoured and their population increases to the point where crop production is disrupted.

It is important to remember that it is not just the farmer who is engaged in food production. Workers in industry who are making tractors, machines, chemicals and fuels are all part of man's manipulation of the environment in the food production process.

Which of the four methods of obtaining food will support:
(a) the largest number of people from a fixed area?
... **Q.7**

(b) the smallest number of people from a fixed area?
... **Q.8**

Food production

The basis of all food production is *photosynthesis*. The sun's energy flows via the green plant to man. Photosynthesis is therefore the most important chemical change on earth which affects all plant growth and not just cultivated plants. Photosynthesis is summarised in the diagram overleaf; study it and make sure you understand it before continuing with the chapter (for more details see *Rural Science 3*).

Photosynthesis: the most important chemical reaction

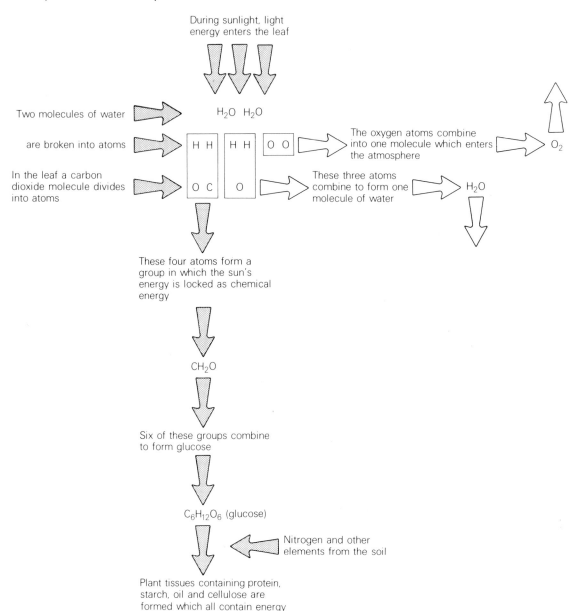

During sunlight, light energy enters the leaf

Two molecules of water

are broken into atoms

In the leaf a carbon dioxide molecule divides into atoms

H_2O H_2O

H H   H H   O O

O C   O

The oxygen atoms combine into one molecule which enters the atmosphere

These three atoms combine to form one molecule of water

O_2

H_2O

These four atoms form a group in which the sun's energy is locked as chemical energy

CH_2O

Six of these groups combine to form glucose

$C_6H_{12}O_6$ (glucose)

Nitrogen and other elements from the soil

Plant tissues containing protein, starch, oil and cellulose are formed which all contain energy which came from the sun

Farming

A person directly responsible for producing our food is called a *farmer* and in order to survive a farmer has to make a profit on the food he grows and he runs his farm for profit. In order to make this profit the farmer must be able to sell the goods he produces; he must therefore grow the food you wish to buy. Governments control the price of most of the farmer's output and therefore have a very big influence on what is grown; they also encourage or discourage the production of certain foods, either by direct control or by giving money to farmers as subsidies.

The type of farming you see in the UK is determined by many different things:

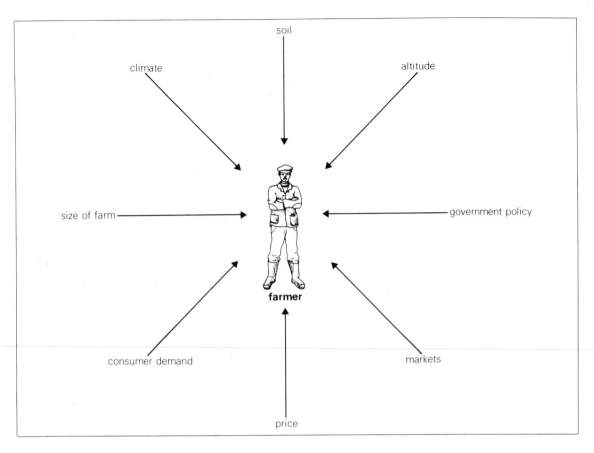

Extensive and intensive farming

Farmers usually concentrate upon the enterprise which suits them and their farms best. Many upland farms are limited to sheep farming where a large area is required to keep a few animals; on this type of farm the output per hectare is very low and it follows that inputs (fuel, fertiliser etc.) must also be low. This type of farming is referred to as *extensive* farming. The opposite to extensive farming is *intensive* farming, where output per hectare is very high and inputs are also very high; one example of intensive production is the use of controlled-environment houses with battery cages for egg production.

Different kinds of farms

On the lowlands there are many types of farms, for example:

1. Grassland and dairy farms.
2. Large arable farms growing cereals.
3. Arable farms growing vegetables.
4. Grassland farms raising livestock.
5. 'Mixed' farms which produce both crops and animal products.
6. Intensive poultry farms.
7. Intensive pig farms.
8. Fruit farms.

6 and 7 use controlled environments in order to convert grain to animal products as efficiently as possible (see *Rural Science 3*). Unlike other farms they do not use the land to grow crop plants; perhaps they should be described not as 'farms' but as factories.

Although the current trend is towards specialisation and a reduction of the number of enterprises, most farms have more than one. For

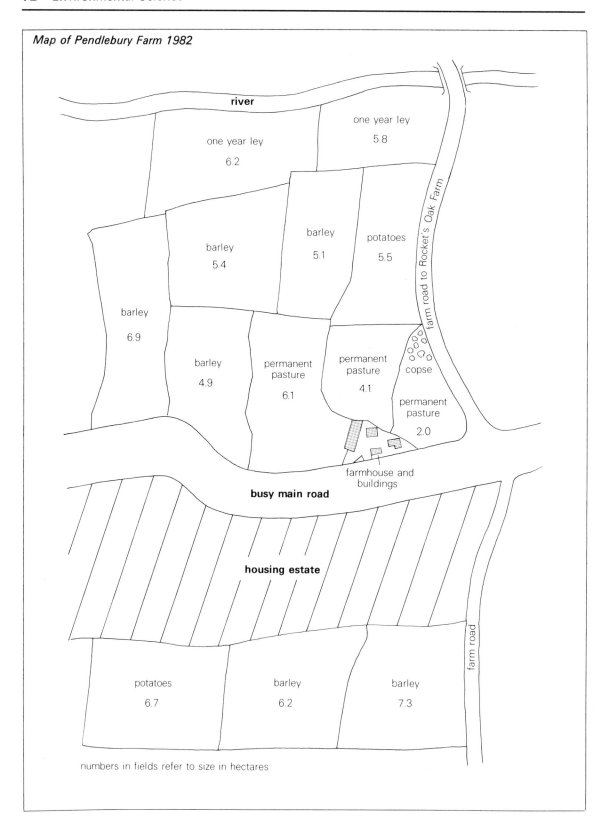

Map of Pendlebury Farm 1982

river

one year ley
5.8

one year ley
6.2

farm road to Rocket's Oak Farm

barley
5.4

barley
5.1

potatoes
5.5

barley
6.9

barley
4.9

permanent
pasture
6.1

permanent
pasture
4.1

copse

permanent
pasture
2.0

farmhouse and
buildings

busy main road

housing estate

farm road

potatoes
6.7

barley
6.2

barley
7.3

numbers in fields refer to size in hectares

example a dairy farm may also rear beef calves or a cereal grower may have a few hectares of fruit and vegetables to supply a local 'pick your own' market.

On the uplands where soils are poor and the climate more hostile, different types of farming are practised; here more sheep are kept and the output per hectare is very much less than in the lowlands. Areas midway between the lowlands and the uplands are called 'marginal' areas and once more the farming pattern is different.

With such a large variety of farms it is not possible to find a 'typical' farm. The best way to learn about food production is to make a detailed study of a farm in your area; the Association of Agriculture (the local National Farmer's Union office will supply the address) will be pleased to provide information.

The study which follows was made by a school in the Midlands and is intended as a model upon which to base your own study.

A study of Pendlebury Farm

Brief description of the farm

Pendlebury Farm adjoins a small market town and is situated on a busy road to the West Midlands conurbation. The farmer is Mr Archer.

Rainfall: 770 mm per annum

Soil: clay loam

Altitude: highest point 70 metres, rolling gently down to 30 metres where the fields join the river

Area: 72.2 hectares including 12.2 hectares of permanent pasture.

Labour: working farmer with one full-time adult employee; some work is done by contractors (people who are hired to bring a machine, do a certain job and then leave).

Implements: 2 tractors, plough, harrow, seed drill, sprayer, fertiliser spreader, foreloader, manure spreader, potato planter, inter-row cultivator, ridge plough, potato harvester, two trailers, hedge cutter, pick-up bailer, mowing machine, hay turner, buck rake, ring and ballast rollers.

Mr Archer's manure spreader

In addition Mr Archer employs a contractor to cut and carry grass for silage (with a forage harvester and grass trailer), also to harvest his barley (with a combine harvester).

Produce: Each year Pendlebury Farm produces 40 tonnes of beef and 200 tonnes of potatoes.

Market: The beef is sold on the hoof (90 head) in the local cattle market where it is purchased by butchers from the West Midlands conurbation. All potatoes are sold 'at the farm gate', i.e. directly to calling customers, in 25-kilo paper sacks; most of the sales are at the weekend and Mrs Archer does the serving.

Crops

Crop rotation

The map shows the cropping pattern in the fields the year the study was undertaken. From year to year, this pattern varies, since because of the dangers of large populations of potato cyst eel worm (*Rural Science 2*) Mr Archer cannot grow potatoes in any one field more often than one year in five. A five-year rotation is practised, which means that during a five-year period a field will have the following crops:

year	1	2	3	4	5
crop	potatoes	barley	barley	grass	barley

Which crop will be grown in year 6?   **... Q.9**

In addition to the permanent pasture, which is kept for the cattle to graze, in any one year there are two fields of potatoes, two fields of temporary grass and six fields of barley.

The year before a field is due to be cropped with a grass and clover ley the seeds are sown at the same time as the barley seeds. The grass and clover seeds germinate and form a layer of vegetation below the seeding barley. After the barley has been harvested the grass and clover ley grows rapidly and is grazed during the autumn. The following spring 250 kg per hectare of inorganic fertiliser is applied to the ley and it is cut for either silage or hay before being ploughed. The grass and clover which is buried during ploughing decays in the soil and increases its fertility.

Barley

When conditions allow, Mr Archer sows winter barley in the autumn; the seeds germinate and the small plants overwinter ready to make rapid growth the following spring as the days become warmer. Any fields not sown in the autumn are sown in spring with spring barley. Winter barley yields crops which exceed 5 tonnes per hectare (t/ha) while spring barley ripens later and produces a somewhat smaller yield.

During the growing period barley is sprayed with a selective herbicide to control the broadleaf weeds, with two fungicides to control fungus diseases and with an insecticide to control aphids. In addition to this the seeds are coated or *dressed* with certain chemicals before sowing to protect them from soil-borne pests and diseases.

After harvest the grain is stored and used to feed the beef cattle. Before being fed the barley is passed through a special machine and *rolled*; this crushes the testa and exposes the contents of the seed to the digestive juices of the animal.

Barley straw is turned with the hay turner to assist drying and then baled with a pick-up baler; bales are stored in a hay barn until required. The straw is used to bed the cattle in the large open yards; a little is eaten but most becomes contaminated with faeces and urine and decays into farmyard manure, which will be returned to the soil.

Potatoes

Mr Archer grows two varieties of early potato (Pentland Javelin and Home Guard) and two varieties of late potato (Wilja, a white potato which is popular with his customers as it makes good chips, and King Edward, an old favourite which boils and mashes very well). Potatoes are planted in March and April as weather conditions allow. Harvesting begins in late June and continues through the summer to meet the farm gate sales. In October the remainder are lifted and stored in clamps in the field adjacent to the farm yard. The fields in which potatoes are to be grown receive heavy dressings of farmyard manure (20 t/ha); in addition 750 kg/ha of complete fertiliser containing 10% nitrogen, 10% phosphorus and 18% potassium are applied just before planting.

The potato crop is sprayed with the contact herbicide paraquat just as the crop is emerging. This kills all the weeds, allowing the potatoes to grow in weed-free conditions; any weeds which germinate later soon die due to lack of light as the potato foliage gives dense cover. In most years the potato crop is sprayed two or three times with a fungicide to protect it against the fungus disease potato blight. Mr Archer has permission to pump 100 000 litres of water per day from the river and use this to irrigate potatoes when it is necessary.

Cattle

Each year in early spring Mr Archer buys 90 reared beef calves which are three months old. The calves are put in the fields to graze; as the quality of the grass declines in the autumn grazing ceases and the cattle are housed in open yards and fed with hay, silage and rolled barley. Soon

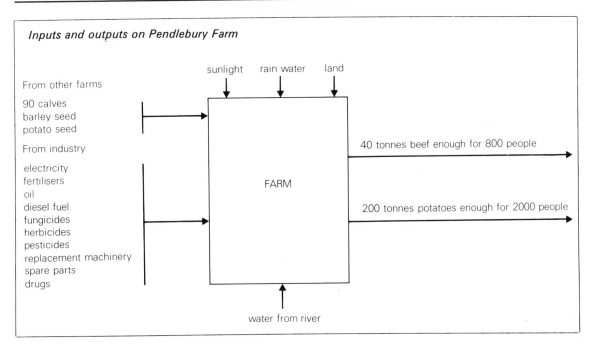

Inputs and outputs on Pendlebury Farm

after Christmas the first cattle are ready for market and weigh between 400 and 500 kg; some cattle are sold each week until the last are marketed in early summer.

Energy flows

There are two major energy flows through Pendlebury Farm:

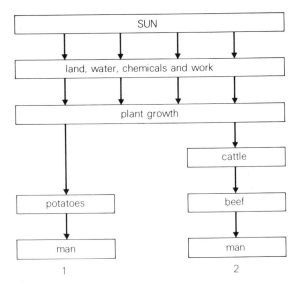

Which energy flow, 1 or 2, will give man the largest proportion of the sun's energy? ... Q.10

Which energy flow, 1 or 2, will give man the largest amount of protein? ... Q.11

Energy flows 1 and 2 above are also food chains. With chain 1 about one-third of the original photosynthetic production is available for man as food. With chain 2 only one-twentieth of the original photosynthetic production is available for man as food.

At what trophic level is man (a) in chain 1?
(b) in chain 2?
... Q.12

How many more people could be fed by this farm if all production was in food chain 1 compared with the number fed if all production was in food chain 2? ... Q.13

The farm in the environment

Effect on wildlife

Mr Archer is interested in wildlife and is aware that his farming has a very big effect on the wildlife in the area. Whenever he sprays his crops with insecticide there will be less food for the insectivorous birds and some of the food which is left may be contaminated with spray residues which then enter the food chain.

The spreading on the fields each year of droppings and bedding from 90 beef cattle increases the population of soil invertebrates, especially earthworms which in turn provide food for rooks. blackbirds, shrews, hedgehogs and other species which live on the farm without affecting its production. The mole is also encouraged by high earthworm populations but these have to be controlled or their hills will cover considerable areas of crop and damage expensive machinery. Mr Archer pays a sum of money each year to the local mole catcher who keeps the mole population down to an acceptable level.

When Mr Archer took the farm fifteen years earlier there was a pond in a field to provide drinking water for the cattle. The wet area around the pond was causing some foot problems with the cattle and the pond was filled in and a mains water supply laid to the field. The loss of this pond must have had a big effect upon the wild life, especially amphibians; when asked, Mr Archer said he thought there were a lot less frogs around than there used to be.

Mr Archer likes to shoot pheasants in the winter and usually grows 1000 m² of 'game mixture' in the corner of a field; this is a mixture of plants which provide shelter and food in the form of leaves (kale) or seeds (maple peas, sunflower and very many more). Finches and linnets no doubt also gain from these sowings, and there are certainly plenty of these birds to be seen, although many will be helped through the winter by bird tables on the local housing estate. Also, in an attempt to encourage the pheasant, Mr Archer leaves the hedge banks unsprayed; these grow a

wide range of wild flowers which provide food for insects, birds and small mammals. The hedges on Pendlebury Farm are cut each year, usually in early winter; this reduces the annual production of hedgerow fruits like blackberries, hips and haws which would otherwise provide food for wildlife.

During the study, seven woody shrubs and climbers were identified in the hedgerows:

hawthorn   bramble
hazel   honeysuckle
elder   dogrose
ivy

and five hedgerow trees:

sycamore
horse chestnut
ash
oak
elm (unfortunately dead)

In each of the nine 30 yard lengths of the hedgerows sampled there were three woody species, it was therefore concluded that the hedges were around 300 years old.

Rats are a continual nuisance on Pendlebury Farm and the problem is getting worse, as they appear to be changing their habits and living in the fields all winter. Barley sown after October is dug up and devoured; some rats are immune to Warfarin (a commonly used rat poison) and the Ministry of Agriculture are advising on how the problems can best be dealt with. Some rats do move into the buildings in the autumn attracted by the cattle food and stored potatoes; two York-shire terriers and three farm cats are allowed to roam free to control these, although unfortunately the cats also catch birds.

Although there are rabbits on the farm their numbers are never high enough to be a nuisance; Mr Archer believes the badgers which live in the copse by the river, the stoats which live in the hedgerows and his own gun (Mrs Archer makes good rabbit pies) prevent numbers increasing to the point where cereal production is affected. (Although the badger is too slow to catch a healthy full grown rabbit, they do catch and eat the very young.)

Flocks of pigeons are attracted to the farm, where they feed on clover during the winter along-side the rooks which are probably feeding on leatherjackets (the larvae of the crane fly). If the pigeons move into the barley fields they are frightened away by a number of rotating bird scaring devices.

Pollution

It was not possible to study pollution but it was noted that the drainage pipes from the fields entered the river and some of the nitrogen fertili-sers applied would be leached from the soil, enter the river and cause some eutrophication downstream (see page 100).

Some of the spray chemicals do no doubt enter the food webs; what effects these have and whether these effects are harmful it is not possible to tell.

Recycling

There is no burning of straw on this farm. All the straw and other crop residues are recycled by being converted to manure by the cattle and spread on the fields or by being directly ploughed in.

The plastic bags in which fertiliser is delivered are sent to David Muat, of Newcastle upon Tyne, where they are processed into raw plastic which is then used to make more fertiliser bags. (Al-though this is a very efficient process which loses only 3% of the original material, only 500 tonnes are recycled in the UK each year out of a possible 25 000 tonnes.)

Effect on landscape

Landscape is the natural scenery of an area. Mr Archer farms in a similar way to his predecessor and, with the exception of filling the pond, has made no changes which have affected the land-scape. His farm is a patchwork of various colours broken up by hedges and trees. The permanent

Hedge removal to create large fields destroys habitats and makes the landscape monotonous

Mr Archer plans to conserve the landscape by screening this new farm building with trees

pasture is always green while the barley fields change from brown to green to gold as the seasons progress.

A change in farm policy could also cause changes in the landscape, for example:

1. if a tower silo was erected to store the grain;

2. if hedges were removed to make fields larger;

3. if the copse was cleared from the end of the small pasture field;

4. if the hedges were left uncut or trees allowed to grow in them;

5. if an orchard was planted; or

6. if more fields were sown with permanent pasture and less crops grown.

Project 5.1

Study a farm in your area using the same headings as the Pendlebury Farm study.

Preserving food

Fresh food quickly deteriorates and becomes unfit for human consumption. Preserving food reduces waste and helps to ensure a continuous supply. The main causes of decay in food are bacteria and fungi; there are, however, other organisms:

Investigation 5.2

Place 1 kg of chicken crumbs (obtainable from most pet shops) in a plastic container and cover with a piece of muslin. Leave the container in a cupboard for about six months after which time the crumbs will be turning into powder. Place a little of the powder on a microscope slide and view under low power. The organisms you will see are many times larger than bacteria and are probably mites or weevils which are living upon the food. These creatures are adapted to live with very little water and survive on the water content of the chicken food, which may seem dry but which contains some 10% water.

Methods of preserving foods

Dehydration

Bacteria, fungi and other organisms of decay cannot survive in very dry environments and dehydrated foods will keep for long periods of time *provided* they are packaged in such a way that they remain dry.

Fruits and vegetables are dried in a cabinet or tunnel through which hot air is circulated. The food to be dried is often exposed to sulphur fumes to retain its colour.

Milk is dried by heating it and forcing it through a fine nozzle into a current of air in an enclosed chamber. The tiny droplets of milk evaporate leaving the solid content to fall to the floor as powder.

Dried foods are almost as nutritious as fresh foods; eggs and milk are almost unaffected but vegetables lose some of the vitamins they normally contain. The appearance is often impaired due to colours fading; to prevent this some vegetables (peas for example) are exposed to sulphur fumes before drying.

Chemical additives

Various chemicals are approved by the government for addition to food. Some of these chemicals reduce the rate at which foods decay and keep it palatable for a longer period of time, while some are added to improve flavour and others to enhance colour. Manufacturers have to inform the consumer when preservatives are being used: on packaged foods the words 'Contains preservatives' can often be seen, also in butcher's shops the sign 'All our sausage contains preservatives'.

Why do chemicals have to be approved by HM Government?   **... Q.14**

Preserving with salt and sugar

When salt and sugar are added to a solution the osmotic pressure increases and, if enough is added, it becomes too great for the organisms of decay to survive. Fruit is preserved with sugar in the form of jam and meat, especially bacon, is preserved with salt.

Experiment 5.1

Fill 100 mm length of visking tubing with tap water and seal both ends by tying. Place the tubing in a beaker of saturated salt or sugar solution. Observe one hour later and answer the question, 'What is likely to happen to bacteria, fungi or other organisms on coming into contact with foods preserved with salt or sugar?'

Note: dried fruit (sultanas, currants, and so forth) contain more water than other dried foods; preservation is due to the high concentration of sugar in the remaining solution.

Canning

Meats, fruits and vegetables are commonly preserved by canning. A can is a *can*ister made of steel which has been coated with tin to prevent rusting and the joints sealed with lead solder. The food is put into the can with *brine* (vegetables) or *sugar syrup* (fruits) and heated to exclude the air; at this point the cans are sealed and then heated in an *autoclave* (industrial pressure cooker) to kill any organisms of decay they may contain. The food inside will keep for months (or even years) depending upon the type of food and the temperature at which it is stored.

Reasons why canned foods may not keep indefinitely:

1. Not enough heat may have been applied to destroy all the enzymes which can cause chemical changes in the food.
2. Some air may remain inside the can and fats become rancid due to oxygenation.
3. The metal of the can and the solder may gradually dissolve.

The length of time cans are heated during canning depends upon the contents. It takes longer for heat to reach the centre of a can of meat than it does to reach the centre of a can of soup. With the former, heat can move only by conduction, while with the latter heat is transferred to the centre of the can by convection currents within the soup. If infra-red heat is used it reaches the centre immediately. Some bacteria form spores which resist temperatures of more than 100 °C for short periods, e.g. *Clostridium botulinum* which causes the fatal disease *botulism*. Foods which may contain this organism are heated to 120 °C and held at this temperature for 30 minutes, whilst this heat will kill the organism it is important to realise that the toxins produced by the bacteria are not destroyed by heat.

Freezing

Unlike heat, cold does not kill all living things; even complex organisms like mammalian embryos can be stored at −196 °C and remain alive. What cold does is to reduce the metabolic rate and effectively prevent the growth of bacteria and fungi; therefore foods which are frozen will deteriorate extremely slowly if kept for long periods in domestic deep-freeze cabinets.

Task 5.2

Most packaged foods contain information about the length of time they may be stored. Make a list of frozen foods and record the storage times. Group the foods into short storage period, medium storage period and long storage period, and see if there is any relationship between type of food and storage period.

Task 5.3

Place a fresh tomato in a deep-freeze cabinet and leave it for 24 hours. On removal the tomato looks exactly as it did when placed in the cabinet except that it is now hard. Allow the tomato to thaw out and compare it with a fresh one. The changes in the frozen tomato are the result of large ice crystals forming during freezing which rupture the walls of the plant cells within the fruit. On thawing, the cells leak and lose their turgidity. It has been found that if foods are cooled very quickly much smaller ice crystals form which are less likely to disrupt the cells. Foods are therefore cooled as quickly as possible when being prepared for storage by freezing, by the method of blasting with cold air, or spreading on cold metal plates, or of immersing in a refrigerating medium.

Remember that the organisms of decay in the food are frozen with it. When the food is thawed they will commence reproduction and decay will begin once more. The number of organisms frozen with the food is kept to a minimum by such processes as *blanching* (immersing in boiling water) and by strict hygiene control when preparing foods for the freezer.

Why must frozen chicken be thoroughly thawed out before cooking? ... Q.15

Other methods of preservation

Deep-freeze cabinets use energy and are expensive to run. The temperature of frozen food will also rise during unrefrigerated transport, causing some deterioration. Methods of storing foods at normal temperatures are being investigated. One such method is sterilising with atomic radiation and another is *freeze drying*. With freeze drying, frozen foods are placed in very low pressure cabinets; this causes the foods to dehydrate by sublimation (ice turning to water vapour without going through the liquid state). If the freeze-dried food is carefully sealed from air and water it will keep for very long periods at room temperature. Freeze-dried foods have the advantage of being very light; they retain their nutritive value and are quickly restored to a fresh state by adding water.

Food processing

In addition to preparing goods for storage, the food industry processes food in other ways, to make it palatable and easy to use. Some foods can be purchased already prepared and cooled; all they require is heating. They are called *convenience foods* as they are very easy to use.

The wheat which leaves the farm does not appear in the shops until it has been processed into bread, flour, cakes, biscuits or breakfast cereals. In most areas it is not possible to buy milk in an untreated form. Milk is pasteurised, sterilised or homogenised before being bottled and in addition the food industry turns it into many kinds of cheese, or into butter, cream, or ice cream. Milk may also be condensed, evaporated or powdered or be made into pudding by adding rice and cooking it in the tin.

All these processes require energy which originates from fossil fuels, and more fossil fuels are used in the kitchen during final preparation. Most foods have received a great many more joules during production, transport and processing than the consumer will obtain from them during digestion (see page 87).

Cod steaks moving along production line to batter mix and freezer

Questions: Food

1. Write single sentences to answer the following questions.

   (a) Which types of farm livestock are most likely to be kept intensively?

   (b) What is a 'mixed' farm?

   (c) From which part of the diet is most energy obtained?

   (d) In what ways does a plant fat differ from an animal fat?

   (e) What percentage of the fertiliser bags used in the UK are recycled each year?

   (f) How does a ley differ from a permanent pasture?

   (h) 'Pentland Javelin' is an early variety of potato, what does this mean?

   (h) Which gas is used during photosynthesis and which is released?

   (i) How many people in the UK are dependent upon one agricultural worker?

   (j) What does a soil scientist mean by the word 'silt'?

2. By farming the land man reduces the numbers and variety of wild plants and animals. What steps can a farmer take to ensure that his operations do not destroy the wildlife of the countryside?

3. (a) What is meant by landscape?
   (b) In what ways can modern farming practice change the landscape?
   (c) What steps could a farmer take to ensure that his operations do not reduce the quality of the landscape?

4. Most foods are produced on a seasonal basis. Name *three* such foods and describe *three* different ways in which *one* of the named foods can be preserved to make it available throughout the year.

5. Chemical fertilisers, herbicides and pesticides have reduced the need for crop rotation on many farms.
   (a) What is crop rotation?
   (b) What are the disadvantages of crop rotation to the farmer?
   (c) What are the advantages of crop rotation to the farmer and to wildlife?

6 Energy

Everything is either matter or energy. Matter has physical substance and whenever matter moves, or changes state, energy is involved. Energy is the means of doing work.

Forms of energy

Energy can exist in several forms: potential, kinetic, chemical, electrical, atomic (or nuclear), radiant, and heat.

Potential energy

Because movement involves energy, any object which might move but is held in position by some resistance is said to have potential energy. For example a boulder on a slope, held by a stone, will move down the slope if the stone is removed although no energy is applied to the boulder.

Kinetic energy

Kinetic energy is the energy a body has by virtue of its movement. For example, a fast-moving cricket ball has kinetic energy; if you stop the ball you absorb this energy: your hand is pushed backwards and becomes warm.

Chemical energy

Any chemical change involves energy (remember photosynthesis). Chemical energy is the energy involved in bonding atoms together to form molecules. A chemical change may take up energy or release energy; a chemical change which takes in energy will release that energy when the chemical change is reversed.

Electrical energy

All atoms contain electrons; electrons may move through a substance, and the energy involved in the movement of electrons is electrical energy.

Atomic energy

Energy is contained within the nuclei of atoms. Man is learning to make use of atomic energy and in *nuclear fission* power stations he splits the nucleus of the uranium atom, releasing some of the energy which bound it together. The source of the sun's energy is atomic but of a different kind; it is nuclear *fusion*, in which four atoms of hydrogen are fused to form one atom of helium (this reaction involves some loss in mass which becomes energy):

$$H_2 + H_2 \rightarrow He$$

Radiant energy

Radiant energy is contained in electromagnetic waves which travel at 3×10^8 metres per second. Light is an example of an electromagnetic wave. The world receives almost all of its energy in this form.

Heat

This is the energy a substance contains by virtue of the movement of its atoms or molecules. (See diagram at top of page 83.)

Measuring energy

The unit of energy is the joule (see page 32); this is a very small amount of energy and it is more usual to use the kilojoule (kJ), which is 1000 joules, or the megajoule, which is 1000 kilojoules.

How many joules in a megajoule? ...**Q.1**

Common units of energy are the *calorie* and its multiple the *kilocalorie*. One calorie = 4.2 joules (1 kilocalorie = 1000 calories). In food science a kilocalorie is called a *Calorie* (i.e with a capital C).

In the home electricity is measured in kilowatt hours (kW h). One kW h of energy is consumed by a single 1000-W bar electric fire burning for one hour; a two-bar fire would consume the same amount of energy in half an hour.

How many kWh of energy are used if a single-bar electric fire burns for eight hours? ...**Q.2**

One tonne of coal has the same amount of energy as 7500 kW h of electricity. One tonne of oil has the same amount of energy as 12 500 kW h of electricity.

In a solid the molecules are in fixed positions vibrating. The hotter the solid becomes the faster the molecules vibrate.

In a liquid the molecules have no fixed positions but move about at random. The hotter the liquid the faster they move.

In a gas the molecules move at very high speed and no longer cling together as happens in solids and liquids. The distances between the molecules is very much greater— a small amount of liquid makes a lot of gas.

Energy conversion

One form of energy can be converted into another; the potential energy of the boulder on a slope becomes kinetic energy as the boulder rolls down. Part of the kinetic energy of the cricket ball becomes heat as you stop the ball with your hand.

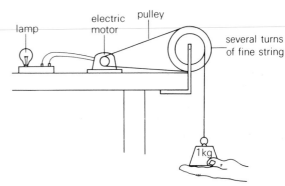

Task 6.1

Study the diagram of the apparatus above and describe all the energy conversions which take place when the hand is drawn away.

Another example of energy conversion:

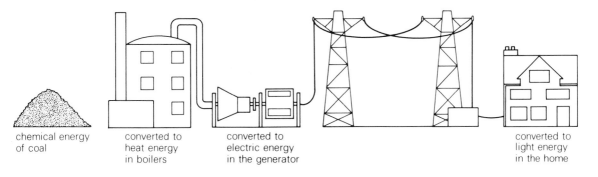

chemical energy of coal

converted to heat energy in boilers

converted to electric energy in the generator

converted to light energy in the home

At each conversion some energy is lost as heat and although one tonne of coal contains 7500 kW h of electrical energy, when burned in a power station it produces only 2300 kW h of electricity. In the electric light not all the electricity consumed is converted to light; a lot is lost as heat, which is why an electric light becomes hot. Note that electricty is not a *source* of energy – it is a *form* of energy which can be converted into motion, heat, and so forth. All the energy in the world eventually becomes heat; this heat is eventually lost to outer space as infra-red radiation. The world is cooling down all the time by this energy loss, which is why it gets cold at night. The energy lost to outer space is balanced by the energy received from the sun which warms the world. On average, the world does not get any warmer nor does it get any colder from year to year; the energy lost therefore must equal the energy received.

We are unable to catch and store the sun's energy; plants alone have the ability to do this by their photosynthesis (see page 69).

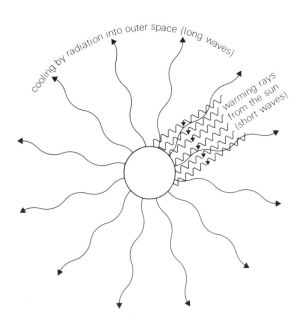

In what form is energy stored in plants? ... Q.3

Fossil fuels

Formation and use

Over 350 million years ago, long before flowering plants had evolved, huge fern forests were growing on the land and converting the sun's energy to chemical energy in their fronds; this was the *Carboniferous* period.

At the same time in the oceans millions of organisms lived on the products of photosynthesis. As the organisms died their bodies became part of the sediment lying among the sands and silt which were to become sedimentary rocks (see opposite page).

These materials – oil, gas and coal – have remained in the earth since that time. Thus the sun's radiation which arrived 350 million years ago is being released today as these materials are extracted and used. A very short while ago (a few hundred years for coal and less than 100 years for gas and oil) man began to make use of these *fossil fuels* in increasing quantities and his civilisation became dependent upon them.

An oil refinery

Oil and natural gas are compounds of hydrogen and carbon called *hydrocarbons*. Natural gas (largely methane: CH_4) can be used without processing; *crude oil* (the substance as it leaves the earth) is a mixture of many different hydrocarbons which have to be separated before they can be used. This separation of crude oil is the work of the *oil refinery*.

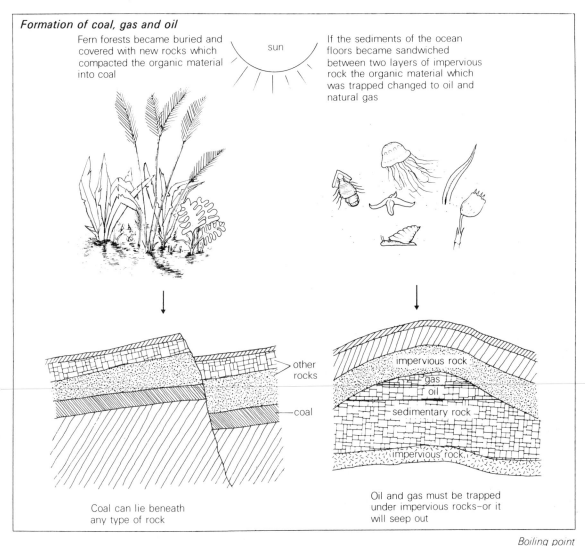

Formation of coal, gas and oil

Fern forests became buried and covered with new rocks which compacted the organic material into coal

If the sediments of the ocean floors became sandwiched between two layers of impervious rock the organic material which was trapped changed to oil and natural gas

Coal can lie beneath any type of rock

Oil and gas must be trapped under impervious rocks–or it will seep out

Oil refinery

Different hydrocarbons have different boiling points and this fact is used to separate them. Crude oil is heated to a gas and fed up a *fractional distillation column*. This column separates the different fractions as they condense; the ones with the lower boiling points are drawn off at the top and those with higher boiling points are drawn off lower down.

Each person (including you) in the UK uses on average the energy from over 6 tonnes of coal each year! This is many more times the energy than is used by a person in a Third World country.

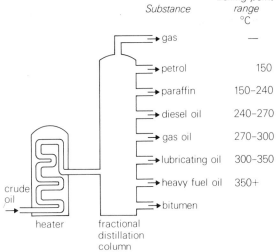

Substance	Boiling point range °C
gas	—
petrol	150
paraffin	150–240
diesel oil	240–270
gas oil	270–300
lubricating oil	300–350
heavy fuel oil	350+
bitumen	

Almost everything we do involves the use of fossil fuel; which of the following does not involve the use of fossil fuel?

Having a shower.

Using an electric light.

Riding in a train.

Walking to school.

Reading a book.

Using a calculator.   **... Q.4**

You may think that sitting in school reading this book has nothing to do with fossil fuel, but this is not true, if the light is on, or the room is heated then fossil fuels are being consumed. Remember also that fossil fuels were used to power the machinery which made the paper and printed the book. Fossil fuels were also used to transport the book to your school; some of the clothes you are now wearing were probably made from oil; and fossil fuels were used to grow and cook the food which is giving you the energy to sit and read.

Not only is man using up energy very rapidly; he is using it in a most wasteful manner – for example, only 15% of the energy that goes into a car's petrol tank is used to drive the wheels!

We live on fossil fuels

Task 6.2

Examine the energy relationships of the baked bean on the opposite page.

The sun's energy input 'M' is released in the boy's body at 'N' and used to provide movement in the form of running.

All the other twelve energy inputs (A–L) required the use of some fossil fuel and the energy inputs from the fossil fuels were very much greater than the energy in the beans.

Write down the letters A–L and by each say which fossil fuel is being consumed at that point to release energy.

Even the humble potato requires a lot of energy inputs from fossil fuels:

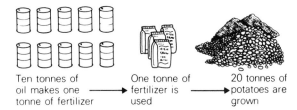

Ten tonnes of oil makes one tonne of fertilizer ⟶ One tonne of fertilizer is used ⟶ 20 tonnes of potatoes are grown

Thus one tonne of oil is required to grow two tonnes of potatoes and the energy in one tonne of oil is much greater than the energy in two tonnes of potatoes (this figure can be much improved by using organic fertilisers such as farmyard manure to reduce the amount of artificial fertiliser required).

Add to this the fossil fuel used to plough, cultivate, spray, harvest and transport the crop; also the fuel used to convert the raw potato to crisps, chips or boiled potatoes. It is easy to see that the energy used in producing a packet of crisps is more than the energy you will obtain from eating them.

If the potatoes were fed to pigs to produce bacon would we obtain more, less, or the same amount of energy from them?   **... Q.5**

Not only do we depend upon oil for transport; we also depend upon oil for food. Mankind in the developed world today is living on fossil fuels.

Experiment 6.1

Processing foods often reduces the amount of energy they contain. To test the hypothesis that processed maize contains less energy than raw maize see diagram overleaf:

1. Set up the calorimeter as in the diagram.
2. Pour in water from a measuring cylinder and record the amount.
3. Weigh the crucible.

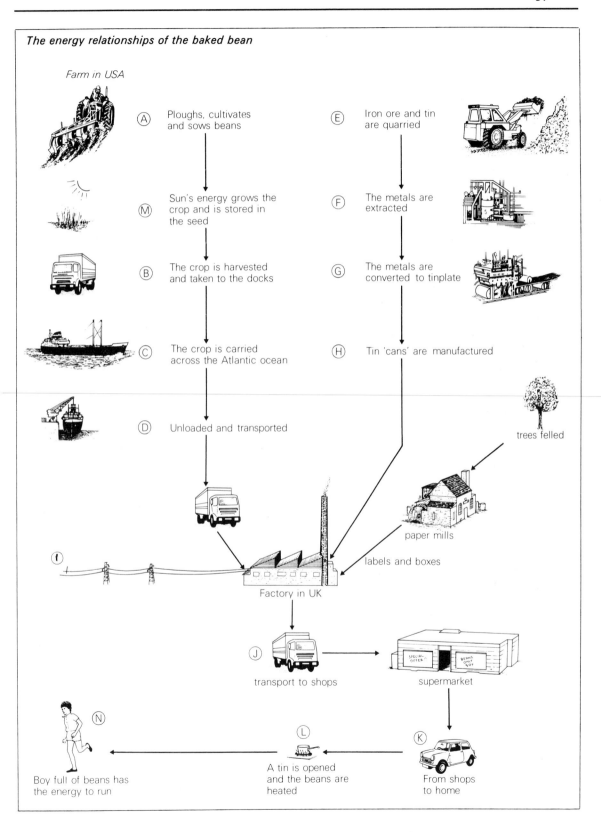

The energy relationships of the baked bean

Farm in USA

(A) Ploughs, cultivates and sows beans

(M) Sun's energy grows the crop and is stored in the seed

(B) The crop is harvested and taken to the docks

(C) The crop is carried across the Atlantic ocean

(D) Unloaded and transported

(E) Iron ore and tin are quarried

(F) The metals are extracted

(G) The metals are converted to tinplate

(H) Tin 'cans' are manufactured

trees felled

paper mills

labels and boxes

Factory in UK

(J) transport to shops

supermarket

(N) Boy full of beans has the energy to run

(L) A tin is opened and the beans are heated

(K) From shops to home

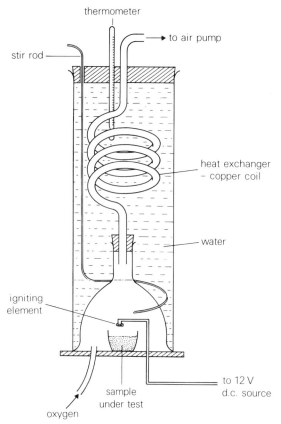

4. Half fill the crucible with dry maize, weigh and replace in the calorimeter.
5. Note the temperature of the water.
6. Turn on the water pump and adjust the flow of oxygen to a very low level.
7. Switch on the electricity and leave on for ten seconds during which time the maize will begin to burn.
8. Ensure an even temperature throughout the water jacket by operating the stir rod.
9. When the maize has completely burned out, continue stirring; observe the thermometer and record the highest reading.

Repeat the experiment using an equal weight of cornflakes.

Calculate the energy produced during each experiment by substituting your readings in the equation:

mass of maize (g) × 4.2 (the thermal capacity of water) × (mass of water + W.E.)

(W.E. is the water equivalent of the calorimeter and will be given to you by your teacher.)

Energy use in the UK

Energy equivalents

Not all fuels contain the same amounts of energy, thus: the energy in 1 tonne of oil = the energy in 1.66 tonnes of coal = the energy in 700 m³ natural gas = 7500 kW h of electrical energy.

The total energy consumed in this country in one year is equal to that contained in 200 million tonnes of oil.

If all this energy came from coal, how many tonnes of coal would be required?   ... Q.6

Recent figures show that the proportions actually used are:

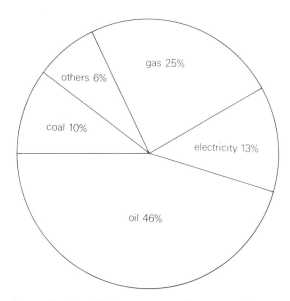

Proportion in which energy supplies are used

These proportions are changing. Why?   ... Q.7

The actual percentage of coal used is larger than the 10% shown above; how do you account for this?
          ... Q.8

Transport however depends almost entirely on oil.

Name two ways in which electricity is used for transport.   ... Q.9

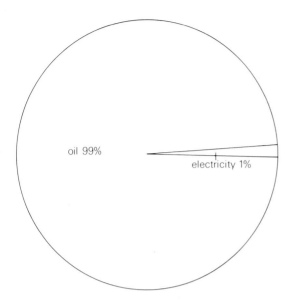

Proportion of energy supplies used in transport

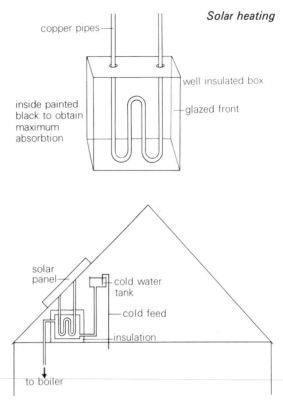

Solar heating

When the sun shines the water which is being fed to the boiler will be warmer than the cold supply and will require less heating

Alternative sources of energy

The conversion of fossil fuels is not the only source of energy available; there are other sources which in theory will last for ever.

Nuclear power

Fifteen per cent of the UK's electricity is generated in nuclear power stations by *nuclear fission*. In this process an atom of Uranium-235 splits into two different atoms of smaller size, and energy is released. One kilogram of uranium releases as much energy as ten tonnes of oil.

There are very great problems with the waste products of nuclear power stations. Highly radioactive liquid waste is stored in cooled steel-clad tanks at Sellafield in Cumbria and (unless new methods are discovered) this will remain dangerous for over 500 years. In addition, a small proportion of highly active elements are produced which may remain dangerous for a million years! The volume of wastes is small but is increasing as the power stations are operating. Other types of nuclear power stations (*fast-breeder reactors*) are being experimented with; these would produce very large amounts of energy from the waste fuels left by the present nuclear power stations. The waste products from fast-breeder reactors are even more dangerous than the waste products from the present nuclear power stations (see page 103).

Solar energy

Energy from the sun drives the hydrological cycle; it also causes winds, waves and tides. Therefore wind, water, tidal and wave power could provide a power source which would last forever and have the advantage of being pollution free. Water power from fast-flowing rivers (which may or may not be controlled by dams and reservoirs) is used in many parts of the world, including the UK (see photograph page 41) to drive turbines connected to generators which produce electricity. Power from this source is called *hydro-electric* power. Ten per cent of the sites suitable for the generation of hydro-electricity in the world are at present being used for this purpose. Some of the sites are in inaccessible areas, long distances from centres of population.

A few areas in the world, one of which is the Severn estuary in the UK, are suitable for harnessing the energy of the tides. A barrier across the estuary could be built which would open and allow the tide in and then close retaining the high water. The water could be made to flow out again in a controlled way through turbines which would be connected to generators. At the time of writing there are no plans to commence this scheme which would cost thousands of millions of pounds.

Wind power has been used for centuries to grind grain, to pump water and to propel ships. The Department of Energy estimates that to provide just 2% of our present needs would require 10 000 wind machines with rotors of 45 metres diameter; the effect of these on the landscape, the noise they would make and the fact that they only work when the wind is blowing make wind power a most unlikely energy source, if they are sited on the land. The Central Electricity Generating Board is experimenting with wind machines called aero generators in the Orkney Islands where winds are more reliable and the possibility of aero generators out at sea is being considered.

Solar heating

Project 6.1

Study the diagram of the solar heating panel (on the previous page) and make one using do-it-yourself materials. The energy absorbed, in joules, can easily be found, by multiplying the volume of water, in millilitres, by the temperature rise, in degrees Celsius, and then further multiplying the product by 4.2.

Even winter sunshine will boil an egg with a well designed panel.

Wave power

Wave power

The Atlantic Ocean produces waves which could possibly be harnessed to produce electricity. Although the waves move along the surface, the water only moves up and down – watch a light piece of debris on water: as waves pass, it moves up and down and does not travel along with the waves.

It may be possible to fix devices shaped like the one in the diagram which would float on the ocean and rock up and down with the waves. This motion could then be converted into electricity. The technology for harnessing wave power on a large scale does not yet exist. Several universities have prototypes ready for testing.

Geothermal

In some parts of the world, hot rocks are fairly near the surface. Cold water can be pumped down into these rocks and pumped up again hot. Some buildings in Paris are heated by this method and there are a few sites in the UK which may be suitable for development, one in Yorkshire and another Cornwall. Drilling holes into hot rocks is taking place in Cornwall and it is hoped to heat water sufficiently by this method to generate electricity.

Task 6.3

Use the figures below to draw a histogram:
Energy consumers in the UK

Domestic	27
Railways	2
Road transport	17
Aircraft	3
Public services	6
Military and other	6
Agriculture	1
Iron and steel	7
Other industry	31

The finite nature of fossil fuels

The earth's crust contains only a certain amount of gas, oil and coal; when it is all used there will be no more. At present rates of consumption gas and oil reserves will be used in your lifetime and known stocks of coal will be all used by 2200, although new deposits are continually being sought:

New deposits are continually being sought

Conserving energy

It therefore makes good sense to conserve as much energy as possible and not waste any. Methods:

Insulation

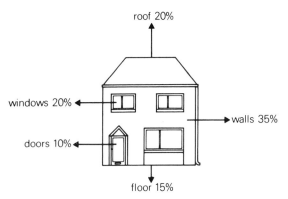

Heat loss from an uninsulated house (the actual percentages will vary with different houses)

A lot of the energy used in heating a house is lost as the heat is conducted through ceilings, walls, floors and windows. Insulation and double glazing prevent much of this loss and less fuel will then have to be used to maintain a reasonable temperature.

Investigation 6.1

To investigate the efficiency of various materials.

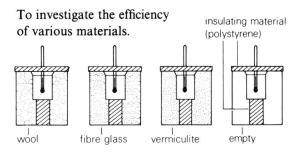

1. Obtain four boxes of equal size and cut four polystyrene stands of *equal* size.
2. Cut four polystyrene lids from a thick sheet and bore a hole in the centre of each just large enough for a thermometer to fit tightly.
3. Pack three boxes with care using different insulating materials and leave the fourth empty as a control.
4. Almost fill each beaker with hot water (say 90 °C).
5. Read and record the temperatures every five minutes until room temperature is reached.
6. Display your results as four line graphs using the same axis and a different colour for each line.

Use of waste heat from power stations

Power stations produce millions of litres of hot water as a by-product; this is usually dumped into the sea, where it may cause thermal pollution, or cooled in the large cooling towers which dominate the landscape. This hot water can be used to provide 'district heating' for all nearby homes and factories (as it is in Moscow), or if the power station is in an unpopulated area the water can be used to heat greenhouses for flower and food production and reduce the amount of fossil fuels at present being used for this purpose. Most power stations are only 30% efficient and using waste heat could make them over 60% efficient.

Reduction of heating in public buildings

Many shops and public buildings (including schools) are at present kept so warm that they are uncomfortable. If the thermostats were turned down a few degrees much less energy would be used.

Car sharing

One of the most wasteful personal uses of energy is the private motor car. Stand by the roadside during the time when people are going to and from work and see what a high proportion of cars are carrying just one person: is this not extremely wasteful? Car sharing schemes reduce the numbers of cars on the road and reduce the pollution caused by the cars.

There are many ways energy can be saved which is at present being wasted; here are some ways in which you can help to conserve the fossil fuels:

1. Put on extra clothes instead of turning up the heating.
2. Never leave a tap running and certainly not the hot tap! (Energy is used to pump water.)
3. Have a shower instead of a bath. (If you have a shower over your bath, the next time you shower put the plug in the bath and see how much water a shower takes compared with a bath.)
4. Turn off the lights when you leave the room.
5. Walk or cycle short distances rather than ask someone to take you by car.
6. Never waste food.
7. Wear your clothes out before you discard them – never discard a sound garment because it is no longer fashionable.
8. Return empty bottles for re-use and take non-returnable bottles to a bottle bank if there is one available.
9. Avoid the purchase of disposable containers.
10. If you purchase a packaged drink choose one in a returnable bottle, not a 'one-trip' bottle or can. (It takes three times as much energy to make an aluminium can as it does to make a glass bottle.) Remember, water is good to drink!

Questions: Energy

1. Write single sentences to answer the following questions.
   (a) What is energy?
   (b) What percentage of the total UK energy consumption is used in agriculture?
   (c) Which energy source drives the hydrological cycle?
   (d) Do the present nuclear power stations obtain their energy by nuclear fission or nuclear fusion?
   (e) Which contains the higher amount of energy, a tonne of oil or a tonne of coal?
   (f) What energy sources are available which do not depend upon fossil fuels?

2. Water runs from a mountain top reservoir, through a hydroelectric power station and into a river. The energy removed from the water is fed into the National Grid as electricity.
   (a) Describe each energy change that takes place during the above sequence.
   (b) Explain how solar energy replaces the water in the reservoir.

3. (a) When did the photosynthesis occur which gave rise to our fossil fuels?
   (b) Use words and diagrams to describe the formation of oil *and* coal.
   (c) Briefly outline *two* different ways in which coal is mined.

4. A considerable amount of research is being carried out to investigate the possibility of using alternative sources of energy.
   (a) What is meant by 'alternative sources of energy'?
   (b) Why is the development of these resources considered necessary?
   (c) Briefly outline *one* 'alternative energy source' and give reasons why you think it may, or may not, be important in the future.

7 Pollution

Look up the word *pollute* in your dictionary. It probably says something like this: 'to make foul, filthy and defile man's environment'. This type of definition covers only the results of long-term or extreme cases of pollution; to the environmental scientist pollution is: 'releasing substances into the environment which cause a change in the eco-system'.

Man has available only two resources:

1. The materials from which the world is made.
2. The incoming radiation from the sun.

The growth of pollution

For millions of years man was part of the natural environment, an omnivore using only natural materials and producing only organic wastes which were recycled by bacteria, fungi and other organisms of decay. During recorded history man has made increasing use of the world's resources and in so doing produces substances he cannot use (wastes).

Industrialisation (still only 250 years old) caused a rapid increase in the quantity and variety of waste products which were disposed of by the easiest and cheapest methods, these were:

1. Dumping on the ground in heaps.
2. Dumping into the seas and rivers.
3. Releasing into the air (where the waste was gas).

It was many years before man realised that these methods of disposal were destroying his environment. Thus in large cities smoke combined with fog formed *smog*, reducing visibility to a few centimetres and causing the death of thousands of people from respiratory disorders. Fish and other life forms disappeared from many rivers and parts of seas and some coasts became covered with oil. Whole areas of land were covered with spoil heaps, rains became so acid it damaged the trees, and in extreme cases whole areas became so poisoned with chemicals that animal and bird life disappeared.

Task 7.1

Study the pollution diagram overleaf (the items not in boxes are pollutants) and answer the questions:

(a) **How many pollutants are listed?** ... Q.1
(b) **Which of the pollutants are gases?** ... Q.2
(c) **Which three of the pollutants are neither solid, liquid nor gas?** ... Q.3

Pollutant gases

Carbon monoxide (CO)

Carbon monoxide is a gas produced when incomplete combustion of carbon-rich fuels occurs:

$$2C \quad + \quad O_2 \quad \rightarrow \quad 2CO$$
$$\text{(carbon)} \quad \text{(oxygen)} \quad \text{(carbon monoxide)}$$

Exhaust gas from cars, cigarette smoke and some industrial processes produce large quantities of carbon monoxide. The pollutant is spread over a wide area and is quickly dispersed into the atmosphere. However, in places where there is traffic congestion the proportion of carbon monoxide in the air rises and often exceeds 100 parts per million (ppm) in busy streets.

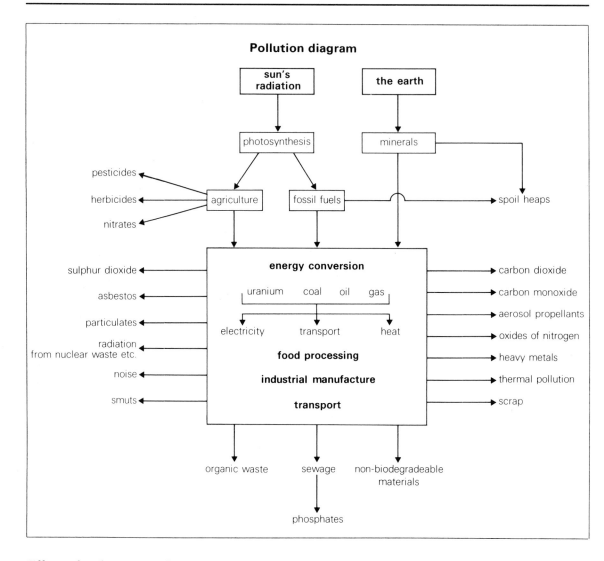

Pollution diagram

Effects of carbon monoxide

Carbon monoxide has little effect on the ecology of an area. It is, however, important as a human poison.

In the lungs, oxygen passes into the blood-stream, where it combines with haemoglobin to form a substance called *oxyhaemoglobin*. The oxyhaemoglobin travels with the blood until it reaches tissue which is low in oxygen. The chemical reaction then reverses and the oxyhaemoglobin releases its oxygen at the site where it will be used. The haemoglobin gets pumped back into the lungs where it will pick up more oxygen.

Direction of reaction depends upon oxygen concentration:

oxygen + haemoglobin $\rightleftharpoons$ oxyhaemoglobin

If carbon monoxide enters the lungs a similar reaction takes place. The carbon monoxide combines with haemoglobin to form carboxyhaemoglobin; however, this reaction is not reversible and so the haemoglobin loses the ability to transport oxygen.

When concentrations of carbon monoxide in the atmosphere exceed 100 ppm, headaches and sickness occur; human beings quickly die if the concentration reaches 1000 ppm. Unlike many poisons carbon monoxide does not accumulate in the body, and lost haemoglobin is quickly replaced in a healthy person.

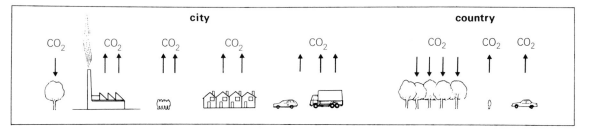

Carbon dioxide (CO_2)

Carbon dioxide is a gas which occurs naturally in the atmosphere at a concentration of about 0.03%; it is an essential compound for photosynthesis and there is a continual exchange of this gas from animals to plants. A proportion of the world's carbon is locked up in the fossil fuels and whenever any of these are burned the carbon they contain is converted into carbon dioxide, which enters the atmosphere:

$$C + O_2 \rightarrow CO_2$$
(carbon) (oxygen) (carbon dioxide)

Effects of carbon dioxide

Thus man's burning of fossil fuel is increasing the concentration of carbon dioxide in the atmosphere. Over 15% of the carbon dioxide at present in the atmosphere has been produced by industry and this percentage is continually rising. It has been estimated that if all the fossil fuels were oxidised (burned) the amount of CO_2 in the atmosphere would increase 17 times.

Carbon dioxide has a 'greenhouse' effect and helps the world to retain a greater proportion of its solar energy receipts; a lot of additional CO_2 in the atmosphere could result in an increase in global temperatures.

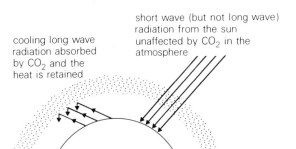

cooling long wave radiation absorbed by CO_2 and the heat is retained

short wave (but not long wave) radiation from the sun unaffected by CO_2 in the atmosphere

This in turn could cause some melting of the polar ice caps, and additional water in the oceans would cover a greater proportion of the earth's surface; there would be less land and many existing climates would change. On a much smaller scale, the temperature in a large city is often a degree or so higher than that of the surrounding countryside; this is due in part to the higher concentration of carbon dioxide in the atmosphere surrounding the city. (It is also caused by heat escaping from buildings, vehicles, electric lights etc.)

The actual increase in atmospheric carbon dioxide is much less than that predicted, as a lot of CO_2 gets dissolved in the oceans.

What effect on temperature would the production of large amounts of smoke have? ... **Q.4**

Sulphur dioxide (SO_2)

Coal, fuel oils and metal ores contain the element sulphur; when these are burned or processed much of the sulphur is oxidised and sulphur dioxide enters the atmosphere:

$$S + O_2 \rightarrow SO_2$$
(sulphur) (oxygen) (sulphur dioxide)

Effects of sulphur dioxide

Sulphur dioxide persists in the atmosphere for some five weeks before combining with more oxygen to form sulphur trioxide (SO_3) which reacts with water to make an airborne form of *sulphuric acid*:

$$SO_3 + H_2O = H_2SO_4$$
(sulphur trioxide) (water) (sulphuric acid)

Rain which contains this acid corrodes iron and steel as well as many building materials. It is also toxic to aquatic life and plants. It is estimated that over 6 million tonnes of sulphur dioxide are discharged into the atmosphere each year in the UK. The Swedish government claims that the prevailing winds blow some of this pollutant to their country, where the resulting acid rains do much damage to the freshwater lakes, coniferous forests and the soil.

Lichen seen growing on this silver birch cannot tolerate sulphur dioxide and so is not seen in industrial areas

Particulates

Particulates are small particles of solids which float in the air. Dust particles are larger than smoke particles, which have diameters of one micron (one millionth of a metre) or less. Particulates enter the air from industrial processes, car exhausts, domestic fires, bare soil, decaying buildings and many other sources.

Effects of particulates in the atmosphere

* Particulates prevent some sunlight from reaching the land and make the weather cooler than it would otherwise be.
* Particulates settle on buildings making them black and dirty.
* Particulates are breathed into our lungs causing bronchial illness.
* Particulates in smoke cause smog.
* Some smoke particulates are hydrocarbons which may cause cancer.

Smoke control zones

Since the Clean Air Act of 1956 the amount of smoke in the UK atmosphere has been reduced considerably by the introduction of *smoke control zones* in which only smokeless fuels may be burned.

Experiment 7.1
To compare unprocessed coal with smokeless fuel

A useful test for sulphur dioxide is that it turns potassium permanganate solution from purple through brown to colourless.

1. Take 150 ml of distilled water and add a *very small* quantity of potassium permanganate crystals, just enough to colour the water pale purple and decant into a beaker. Divide the solution from the beaker into three equal parts in three boiling tubes.
2. Set up two lots of apparatus as shown in the diagram, including one boiling tube of potassium permanganate solution in each. (The third tube of potassium permanganate is kept for colour comparison purposes.)

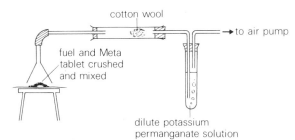

3. On one gauze place a Meta solid fuel tablet and 50 g of crushed coal.
4. On the other gauze place a Meta solid fuel tablet and 50 g of crushed smokeless fuel. (The type used on *open* fires.)
5. Turn on the air pumps and light both lots of fuel.
6. Allow both experiments to run until the fuel is burned out.
7. Examine both lots of cotton wool for particulates and compare.
8. Compare the colours of the potassium permanganate in the boiling tubes.

Oil

Accidents with oil tankers, dumping of unwanted oil in oceans by ships, and accidents while extracting oil from the sea bed release masses of oil which float on the surface of the oceans for a while before they are lost through evaporation and sinking. These floating masses are called *slicks*. Slicks cause damage to coastline environments, to marine life and to terrestrial wildlife.

The most obvious form of wildlife affected by oil is seabirds, particularly cormorants, gannets and terns which have to dive through the floating oil to obtain food from the sea. Thousands of birds die from oil pollution each year; a few are rescued and cleaned with detergents, but unfortunately many of the cleaned birds die shortly after release and the RSPB on principle do not revive affected birds.

What do the letters RSPB stand for?   **... Q.5**

Investigation 7.1
To find out the effect of crude oil on feathers

1. Obtain some feathers; include flight feathers, down feathers and coverts.
2. Take a flight feather and using a pipette dropper add a little water to the feather and observe.
3. Use a second pipette and add a drop of crude oil; observe.

The two liquids behave in different ways as the surface tension of water is much greater than the surface tension of oil.

4. Examine a clean part of the feather under a microscope and compare this with the part covered with oil.
5. Weigh a clean flight feather using a top pan balance or similar sensitive instrument.
6. Carefully cover the feather with oil, making sure there is no surplus and reweigh. How much oil does the flight feather hold?
7. Attempt to clean the feather with detergent (washing-up liquid). How difficult would it be to clean a whole bird?
8. Test a cleaned feather with a drop of water and compare with 2.

Noise

Noise is any sound which is unpleasant and annoying.

Sound travels through the atmosphere as waves of compression. It can be defined and measured scientifically; it has *loudness*, which depends upon the amount of energy involved, and *frequency*, which is the number of waves per metre.

Noise can be difficult to measure as people disagree about what is noise and what is not. For example, you may find disco music very enjoyable but other people may find it to be an intolerable noise. Some people enjoy silence, while others prefer to have sound in the background all the time (a radio etc.). Sounds which are 'noise' in one place may be perfectly acceptable in another, for example the sounds of the playground would be noise in the classroom.

Measurement of noise

Noise is measured in decibels (dB), one decibel being the smallest change in loudness that the average person can detect. An increase of ten decibels is judged to give a twofold increase in loudness. The human ear is not equally sensitive to all frequencies and the highest frequencies which can be heard are often unpleasant – high-pitched shrieks, the sound of fingernails on glass, or a spoon squeaking on a plate.

Using a sound meter

Sound meters designed to measure noise use the dBA scale which takes into account both factors which make noise – loudness and frequency.

1. In the quietest area available, create a constant level of noise, e.g. start a power-driven lawn-mower and leave the engine to run.
2. Using a sound meter take dBA readings at measured distances from the noise, from 0 to 100 metres.
3. Plot the results on a line graph and discover the relationship between noise and distance.

Experiment 7.2

1. Set up a constant noise as in the previous experiment.
2. Fix a sound meter about five metres away from the source.
3. At a measured distance from the sound meter place sheets of equal thickness of a variety of materials in the path of the noise.
4. Discover which type of materials form the most effective sound barriers.

5. Repeat this experiment using as a barrier varying thicknesses of sheets of one material.
6. This experiment may also be adapted to find the best gap between two sheets of glass if double glazing is required for sound proofing.

Typical sound levels of common noises:

	Decibels
Silence	0
Talking quietly	25
Talking loudly	65
Radio with volume high	85
Motorcycle accelerating	95
Pneumatic drill	125
Pain is experienced at	130

Preventing noise nuisance

Excessive noise causes deafness; it also increases stress which may lead to other types of illness. The Noise Advisory Council claim that road traffic is the biggest single source of noise nuisance; they also say that 11% of all houses in this country are subject to higher levels of road traffic noise than is considered by the government to be acceptable. Solid barriers, double glazing and tree planting all help to improve the environment by deadening noise. Legislation limits the amount of noise which new cars and lorries can make and night flights are banned at many airports.

Double glazing

Lead

Lead is a heavy metal which causes death if taken in fairly large quantities and in smaller quantities lead can cause permanent brain damage to babies and young children. This causes reduction of intelligence, apathy, loss of appetite, anaemia and abdominal pain.

Man's activities cause considerable quantities of lead to enter the environment. Some of this lead enters the human body through the digestive and respiratory systems. Once inside the body, lead is carried on the surface of red blood cells and 95% is deposited in the bones. Some lead is excreted in faeces and urine and some grows out with the hair.

Sources of lead in the air

1. *Paint* Much paint (including road markings) contains lead and as it weathers small particles enter the atmosphere as dust.
2. *Certain industrial processes*, e.g. lead works at:

   Market Harborough   Abbey Wood
   Chester   Thorpe (Leeds)
   Gravesend

The lead contained in ferrous scrap may be released on remelting. The burning of old lead-acid battery cases after the lead has been removed in small scrap yards, releases lead.

3. *Combustion of coal* Burning coal produces some lead but the amounts are very small when compared with lead from other sources.

4. *Petrol fumes and exhaust gases* In 1980, in the UK, 10 000 tonnes of lead were added to petrol to increase the octane rating and prevent 'knock' in engines. 7000 tonnes of this lead was emitted as fine particles with the exhaust gases into the atmosphere. Most of this lead is dispersed over a very wide area, but on busy urban roads the concentration is often as high as 6 micrograms of lead per cubic metre of air (μg/m^3). Large particles of dust are deposited near the car exhaust but fine particles remain in the air for long periods and small quantities have even reached the polar regions: thus ice formed in 1950 contains 0.02μg/m^3 lead whereas that formed in 1980 contains 0.2μg/m^3 lead, which is ten times as much.

Task 7.2

Concentrations of lead in the air measured at various distances from the side of a busy urban motorway appear in the chart below.

Display these results on a line graph. The distance goes on the horizontal axis.

This source of pollution is declining due to legislation by governments; during the decade 1971 to 1981 the maximum amount of lead allowed in petrol in EEC countries has been reduced from 0.84 g/litre to 0.4 g/litre.

It is hoped that by 1985 it will not exceed 0.1 g/litre and that future car engines will be designed to run with lead-free petrol, which will be available at petrol stations in 1990. In present engines lead makes the fuel *burn* in a *controlled* way; if lead-free petrol was used the fuel would *explode*, creating a pressure before the piston was at the top of its stroke, which would wear out engines more quickly and waste fuel.

Lead in food

Very much more lead enters the body from food than from the atmosphere.

Average daily intake of lead in food in the UK
Adults   100 μg   (μg = microgram)
Children 2–4 years   70 μg
Bottle-fed babies   50 μg
Breast-fed babies   1.5 μg

Distance from motorway (m)	0	10	25	50	75	100	150	200
Concentration of lead in air (μg/m^3)	12	8	5	2	1.8	1.6	1.3	1

The WHO (World Health Organisation) states that the maximum safe level for adults is 430 µg per day. Food offered for sale in the UK may not contain more than one part per million of lead (1 mg/kg in food)

Sources of lead in food:

1. Lead water pipes and lead-lined storage tanks contaminate water used for drinking and preparing food.
2. Glazed containers.
3. Polluted air contaminates food.
4. The use of lead solder in the manufacture of cans for canned foods.
5. The use of sewage sludge as fertiliser. Lead enters sewage from industry, road run-off and domestic discharge and is not removed by any of the sewage works processes.

Some 50% of the lead in the diet comes from water which is either drunk or used for cooking vegetables and 15% from tin cans (canned beverages contain very much less lead than canned foods). Canned baby foods however contain no lead from this source as manufacturers of these products use pure tin solder.

In a house plumbed with lead pipes, water drawn first thing in the morning contains a higher concentration of lead than that drawn later in the day. Why is this? ... Q.6

Name two materials which are replacing lead for domestic water pipes. ... Q.7

Eutrophication

This word describes the addition of plant nutrients to an area which upsets the ecological balance. Eutrophication most commonly affects water habitats and the main pollutants are nitrogen and phosphorus.

Sources of pollutants

A. Farmers spread various fertilisers on fields to increase crop production. Most of these fertilisers contain nitrogen compounds which are soluble and move with the drainage water through the soil. The drainage water, with its dissolved nitrogen salts, goes via ditches and streams into lakes and rivers.
B. Raw sewage contains phosphorus which comes from detergents and human faeces. Normal sewage treatment does not remove phosphorus which remains in the effluent and is discharged into the river or sea.

Effects of pollutants

Nitrogen and phosphorus are important plant nutrients. When these two elements enter the water they cause the algae to grow very rapidly (rapid algal growth is called a *bloom*) with the following results:

1. Algae float near the surface. An increase in algae prevents light from penetrating the water, and bottom-rooting plants, deprived of light, quickly die.
2. An increase in the numbers of algae results in an increase in the numbers of dead algae. This in turn causes an increase in the numbers of bacteria which live upon dead algae.

3. The increase in the bacterial population lowers the oxygen content of the water.
4. The reduction of the level of oxygen in the water causes the deaths of the larger aquatic animals.

Oxygen levels required by different species of fish (see also page 63)

Oxygen content of water	Species of fish present		
Very high	trout	minnow	bullhead
High	chub	perch	
Medium	roach	pike	
Low	carp	tench	bream

The Norfolk Broads

This is an area with a special eutrophication problem. The Norfolk Broads consists of 5 rivers

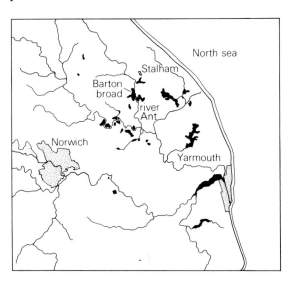

and 46 flooded ancient peat diggings ('broads') which cover some 3600 hectares. The rivers and 14 broads are open to public navigation and many thousands of people spend holidays in the 6500 pleasure boats which are available for hire.

Look at the section through a broad.

Why are there no snails in deposits which have accumulated after 1950?   ... Q.8

Norfolk broads
Section through a broad

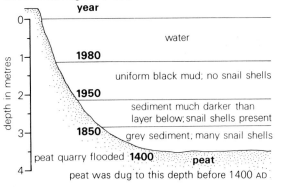

Effects of eutrophication

These are as follows:

1. The light is cut off to underwater plants due to rapid algal growth.

2. The underwater plants die.
3. Surface waves, caused by wind, are no longer damped down by underwater vegetation and they reach the reeds with a much greater force.
4. The reeds cannot tolerate the increased waves and die out leaving the banks exposed.
5. Having lost the protection of the reeds the banks crumble away and nearby land is flooded.
6. Species which depend upon a reed bed for their habitat die out.

Bank protected by reeds

An unprotected bank showing exposed tree roots

Vegetation which grew upon the bottom of the broads anchored the silt and prevented it from being washed downstream. The loss of bottom vegetation through eutrophication means that there is nothing to anchor the silt which gets washed to other areas where it may impede navigation.

The 6500 holiday craft add to the problem in the following ways:

1. The boats' propellors stir up the sediment making the water even more opaque.
2. The wash from the boats also kills the reeds and destroys the banks.

3. Phosphate-rich washing-up liquid and other detergents, are deposited in the water increasing the eutrophication problem.

The loss of much of the Norfolk reed beds has caused serious decline in animal life which depend upon this type of habitat; examples are the bittern and the marsh harrier, which have become extremely rare in this area where they were once common. (In 1950 there were 60 pairs of bitterns; in 1980 there were 3 pairs.)

A counter-measure

In an effort to reduce eutrophication in the Broads, one sewage works is conducting an experiment in phosphate stripping. Before the final sewage effluent is discharged into the River Ant it is treated with ferric sulphate; this combines with the phosphates into solid particles which are removed in a settlement tank. Ninety per cent of the phosphate present in the sewage is being removed in this way and the effects of its removal are being studied in Barton Broad.

Atomic radiation

Radioactivity and half-life

Radioactive elements have very large atoms and gradually decay into other elements with small atoms; this decay produces energy in the form of heat and the radiation of particles from the atom. Radioactive elements occur naturally in some rocks and they decay at different speeds; the speed of decay is measured in *half-life*; if a radioactive substance loses half its weight in one year then it is said to have a half-life of one year. This does not mean that it will all be gone in two years: consider 64 g of a radioactive substance with a half-life of 10 years:

Years later	10	20	30	40	50	60
Weight of substance remaining	32	16	8	4	2	1

What weight will be left after 70 years?   ... Q.9

Hazards to health

Our bodies are subject to radioactive radiation from the earth and from the sun; this naturally occurring radiation amounts to a dose each year of 100 millirads. In addition we receive 19 millirads of radiation from man's activities; medical (X-rays, radium treatment etc.), military (fallout from nuclear bomb tests), industry and nuclear power. This total of 119 millirads is called *background* radiation and is in itself harmless. However, large amounts of radiation are extremely harmful, causing damage to organs, blood and bones, sterility, genetic damage and death. Radioactivity cannot be detected by any of the human senses.

People who are likely to be subjected to radiation at work, (e.g. operators of X-ray equipment) wear a device which monitors the amount of radiation they receive, if this becomes too high they are moved to other employment for a period of some months.

Nuclear weapons tests

In the 1950s and early 1960s some countries (including our own) were exploding atomic bombs in the atmosphere in order to test them. 'Fallout' (radioactive pollution) from these tests spread over the whole world. This fallout included a substance called *strontium 90*.

Strontium 90 with a half-life of 19 years was being deposited in childrens' bones. As bone marrow manufactures blood cells, the dangers of these children developing leukaemia was one of the many health risks caused by pollution with radioactive substances. In 1963 the Test Ban Treaty was signed by several countries, including the USA and USSR, the major nuclear powers, agreeing not to test nuclear explosive devices in the atmosphere (although they still test them underground).

Nuclear power stations

In nuclear power stations the combustion of the uranium fuel produces other radioactive substances. Substances which consist of low-radiation gases are disposed of by discharging them into the atmosphere. Liquids with low radioactivity are dumped in the sea. Some other substances produced are extremely radioactive and dangerous; one of these is the material from which atomic bombs are made, plutonium 239, which has a half-life of 24 000 years! Dangerous liquids are stored in tanks which are kept cool and shielded by masses of concrete. These liquids must be kept for many hundreds of years – this is a massive problem which is getting worse.

Why is the problem of safe storage of radioactive wastes becoming worse? ... **Q.10**

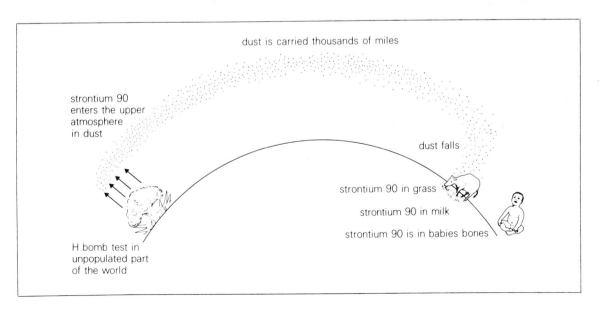

dust is carried thousands of miles

strontium 90 enters the upper atmosphere in dust

dust falls

strontium 90 in grass

strontium 90 in milk

strontium 90 is in babies bones

H bomb test in unpopulated part of the world

Experiment 7.3

(Make observations and records twice each week.)

1. Purchase packets of sunflower or barley seeds which have been irradiated with different levels of radiation (obtainable from suppliers of scientific equipment):

(r = röntgen – a unit of radiation)

2. Fill a subdivided seed tray with seed compost and sow one row from each packet, two seeds in each section 10 mm deep:
3. Label as shown and place in a greenhouse; water as necessary.
4. When most of the successful plants are 50 mm tall, pot on into 150 mm pots. (See *Rural Science 3*, pages 47–8.)
5. Grow the plants on until they flower.

Tabulate the results like this:

Level of radiation	Percentage germination	Number to reach 100 mm	Number which flower	Other observations

Aerosols

The products in the container opposite are packed under pressure with an inert gas (Freon) which propels them through the small nozzle at the top. The gas escapes into the atmosphere and may eventually rise to the stratosphere, where it could reduce the amount of ozone present. (In its liquid state Freon has a vapour pressure which is greater than atmospheric pressure.)

What effect would the reduction of ozone in the atmosphere have on life on earth? ... **Q.11**

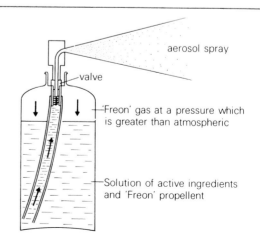

aerosol spray

valve

'Freon' gas at a pressure which is greater than atmospheric

Solution of active ingredients and 'Freon' propellent

Task 7.3

List as many materials as possible which are packed in aerosol containers. If you have less than twenty, think again.

Pesticides

Man regards organisms which may reduce his food supply as pests and he goes to great lengths to limit their numbers. Many insects are pest species and man wages chemical warfare against them. Chemicals which kill insects are called *insecticides*, of which there are three main types:

1. Inorganic poisons, e.g. lead arsenate.
2. Naturally produced organic substances, e.g. 'derris dust' the ground root of the derris plant (this is also very poisonous to fish) and pyrethrum (extracted from the flower of an African species of chrysanthemum).
3. Synthetic organic substances (e.g. DDT and BHC).

Use and effects

The inorganic poisons have been replaced by organic ones and are now little used.

The natural products are very effective and have the advantage that they are soon destroyed by the normal process of biological decay.

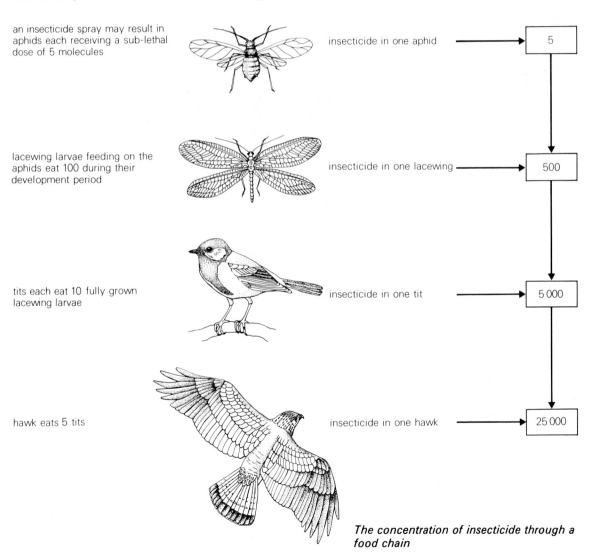

an insecticide spray may result in aphids each receiving a sub-lethal dose of 5 molecules

insecticide in one aphid   → 5

lacewing larvae feeding on the aphids eat 100 during their development period

insecticide in one lacewing → 500

tits each eat 10 fully grown lacewing larvae

insecticide in one tit → 5 000

hawk eats 5 tits

insecticide in one hawk → 25 000

The concentration of insecticide through a food chain

The synthetic organic compounds are very effective and widely used throughout the world. Several of these compounds have the serious disadvantages that they are not *biodegradable* (that is, living organisms do not break down the molecules they contain into simpler substances) and will not decay or rot away. Living organisms are unable to excrete many of the synthetic organic insecticides which therefore remain in the tissues of the organism. The retained chemicals become concentrated along the food chain, and a small amount in the tissues of the herbivore can become a lethal dose for the top carnivore (see diagram on previous page).

This may or may not be a lethal dose for the hawk. If it is not a lethal dose it will certainly have some harmful effects. DDT, for example, upsets the shell-producing gland in the peregrine falcon; this leads to thin-shelled eggs which are unlikely to withstand the incubation period.

In many countries (including our own) the use of DDT is either banned or strictly controlled. Liberal use during the middle part of this century distributed it throughout the biosphere and it can now even be found in the fat of the Antarctic seabirds.

Alternatives to pesticides

Modern food production would be impossible without the use of chemicals. If all agricultural chemicals were banned tomorrow production would fall by well over half, which we cannot afford in a world where the population could outstrip food supply.

Other methods of pest control are possible and much research is being carried out to make them possible.

Greenhouse whitefly

A common pest of greenhouse plants is small white fly only 1 mm long. The body is yellow, the eyes black, and the wings white. The adult flies spend most of their time on the underside of leaves but will take off if disturbed.

Both adults and larvae feed by sucking sap from the leaves of plants; the loss of sap weakens the

White fly on tomato leaf

plants and reduces their growth. In addition the insects excrete a sticky substance (honeydew), rich in sugar, which interferes with the normal function of the leaf. A black fungus grows in the honeydew, spoiling the appearance of the plants and fruit and preventing light from reaching the leaves.

Tomatoes, cucumbers, chrysanthemum, dahlia, fuschia, salvia and many more plants are subject to whitefly attack (see photograph above).

Biological control (control using biological methods)

Many years ago a Hampshire gardener discovered whitefly larvae which were black on the leaves of his tomato plants. He sent the leaves with the black larvae to a horticultural research station where they found that, instead of producing whitefly, a black larva produced a tiny wasp. Observing the female wasp they found that she visited about 50 whitefly larvae during her 14 day life, and laid an egg in each one. Inside each larva the egg hatched into a wasp larva which consumed the insides of the whitefly larva, killing it and turning it black. The wasp larva pupated inside the whitefly and emerged as an adult a few days later.

The wasp was named *Encarsia formosa* and during the 1930s it was widely used to assist whitefly control in greenhouses. During the 1940s new insecticides were discovered and the use of *Encarsia formosa* was discontinued. More recently the dangers of the liberal use of insecticides have been realised and once more *Encarsia formosa* is being used to control whitefly in greenhouses.

It is possible to buy tobacco plant leaves upon which are whitefly larvae which contain the parasite *Encarsia formosa*. These are hung in the greenhouse above the whitefly-infested plants; a few days later the wasps emerge and begin laying eggs in the whitefly scales. If the correct numbers of *Encarsia* are introduced the whitefly population will be reduced to a level where their numbers do not affect the vigour of the tomato plants.

Other methods of biological control

The breeding of resistant strains.
Some varieties of crop plants are more resistant to diseases than others. The serious disease of potatoes, wart disease, has been virtually eliminated by this method.

Work is currently being carried out to introduce a gene from a wild South American potato which would give the foliage of our heavy cropping varieties sticky hairs. Aphids would be unable to feed upon potato leaves with sticky hairs; this would protect the crop from the endemic virus diseases from which it now suffers, such as potato leaf roll (see photograph below), as aphids transmit the causative organism.

A healthy leaf (left) and diseased leaf (right)

The breeding in captivity of very large numbers of males of a pest species and sterilising them with radioactive isotopes is a form of biological control. The sterilised males are released into the countryside where they mate with wild females, but with no effect. An insect parasite of cattle called 'screw worm' has been controlled in America by this method.

Questions: Pollution

1. Write single sentences to answer the following:
   (a) Which part of the body is damaged by carbon monoxide?
   (b) In what way may an aerosol harm the environment?
   (c) Which two chemical fertilisers are most likely to cause eutrophication?
   (d) Why are baby food tins sealed with a different solder than other food tins?
   (e) What substance is added to petrol to control engine 'knock'?
   (f) In what units is noise measured?
   (g) How may an oil slick originate?
   (h) What does the Noise Advisory Council consider to be the biggest single source of noise nuisance?

2. Explain how the increased use of fossil fuels during the last 200 years has created a parallel increase in environmental pollution.

3. Write about the pollution caused by a *named* heavy metal under the following headings:
   (a) Damage caused.
   (b) Pathways by which the metal enters the environment.
   (c) Possible ways of reducing pollution from this source.

4. (a) Explain why the introduction of a quantity of nitrogenous fertiliser into an aquatic environment reduces the oxygen content of the water.
   (b) What is an 'agal bloom' and how is it likely to affect submerged vegetation.

5. (a) What is meant by the 'half-life' of a radioactive substance?
   (b) What weight will remain after 125 years of 128 grams of a radioactive substance which has a half-life of 25 years?
   (c) Explain how the testing of atomic weapons in the Pacific Ocean affected babies in the UK before the Test Ban Treaty was negotiated.

8 Population

A *population* is the total numbers of species in a certain area. Populations do not normally remain static but are continually either increasing or decreasing – they are dynamic – and the study of these changes is called *population dynamics*. One reason for population increase is that all species, both plant and animal, have the potential to produce more offspring than is required to replace them when they eventually die.

Investigation 8.1

Collect a plant with pods on such as rose-bay willow-herb, vetch, shepherd's purse. Count the number of pods, flowers and flower buds. Take off ten mature pods, open them and count the seeds to find the average number of seeds per pod. Multiply the average seeds per pod by the total number of pods, flowers and buds to find the total number of seeds the plant would have produced.

How many seeds were required to grow the plant you collected? ...Q.1

Investigation 8.2

Take five plastic cups approximately 200 ml in size and make a hole in the bottom of each by trimming off 20 mm from the bottom edge. Almost fill the pots with John Innes seed compost and sow radish seeds as follows:

Pot number	1	2	3	4	5
Number of radish seeds	1	3	10	25	50

Place the pots in the school greenhouse or classroom window and observe their growth. Grow them on until seeds are produced. Record your observations, discuss the results with your teacher and read from the Bible, *Matthew*, Chapter 13, verses 1–8.

Animal populations

Rabbits

A pair of tame rabbits, carefully fed and cared for, can easily produce 40 offspring in a single year. If these offspring were allowed to breed, by the end of the following year there could be over 1000 rabbits, all from a single pair.

In nature, however, such an increase would be extremely unlikely because:

1. Many of the young would be eaten by predators – owl, fox, badger, stoat etc.

2. The amount of food available varies with the seasons and if the mother is not well nourished during early pregnancy the young die in the uterus and are re-absorbed into the mother's tissues.

3. Some would die from disease – the more crowded the rabbits the more likely the disease.

4. As rabbit numbers increase they would pollute the area around their burrows, food plants would die out and be replaced by moss or nettles.

5. The digging of burrows would prevent yet more ground from producing food.

6. There would not be enough room for does to make nests.

Herds of cattle also increase in numbers, yet the cow has only one calf in a year – from where does the increase come?   ...Q.2

Where only small numbers of offspring are produced the parent has to take good care of them or the species would die out.

Owls

Recent study of owls in a woodland area in Oxfordshire has led scientists to believe that populations are controlled by the amount of food available. In other words it is not the number of owls which control the numbers of small rodents but it is the number of small rodents which control the numbers of owls. (Owls of course eat rodents.) Less rodents means less owls and more rodents means more owls. When the numbers of rodents decline two things happen to the owls:

1. Less young are reared as the parents are unable to find enough food for both themselves and their young. This is particularly true of young inexperienced parents.

2. The dominant owls increase the size of their territories; this gives them a larger area in which to hunt and presumably a bigger food supply. It also reduces the number of territories and therefore the number of owls in a wood.

Human populations

The number of owls in a certain area of Oxfordshire has no effect upon the number of owls in Australia. With people it is different, as they can and do travel long distances in large numbers. People also move food around in vast quantities. For example, half of the food eaten in this country is grown abroad. Thus when studying human populations the total world population is more important than the population of a single country which may be subject to change by immigration and emigration.

Collecting statistics

The study of human populations is based upon statistics and statisticians require accurate numbers with which to work. In the United Kingdom the figures are obtained in the following ways:

1. Every ten years there is a national census which counts the number of people and collects information about their age, sex and marital status. The last census was taken in 1981 and the next should be in 1991.
2. All births are registered.
3. All deaths are registered.
4. All marriages are recorded.
5. All divorces are recorded.

Many other countries also collect and record similar information; some do not, however, and for this reason world population figures are based upon surveys and a good deal of estimation by the demographers (people who study human populations). One of the reasons why detailed information is collected about populations is that governments need to plan ahead to provide facilities such as houses, roads, hospitals and schools.

As the UK was the first country to become industrialised, the population changes which followed are of very great interest, as this appears to be the pattern which is also happening in other countries following their industrialisation.

Birth rate and death rate

To understand the changes in population in the UK during the last 200 years it is necessary to use the quantities *birth rate* and *death rate*:

Birth rate, called *natality* by demographers, is the number of people born each year per 1000 head of population.

Death rate, called *mortality* by demographers, is the number of people who die each year per 1000 head of population.

What happens to the total population if
(a) birth rate exceeds death rate?
(b) death rate exceeds birth rate?
(c) the birth rate is equal to the death rate?
                                   ...Q.3

Consider the graph in four sections opposite:

(a) Birth rate and death rate were both very high (a little over 30); as the birth rate was slightly higher there was a steady increase in population.

(b) Increased medical knowledge, better health, better sanitation and cleaner water caused a big fall in the death rate; the birth rate remained high, causing a rapid increase in population.

(c) Desire to limit family size coupled with knowledge of birth control reduced birth rate which fell until it was similar to death rate. Rate of population increase fell sharply, but population continued to increase slowly.

(d) Birth rate and death rate fluctuated at similar levels giving a more or less stable population.

Population pyramids

The information about age and sex collected by the national census is used by demographers to construct *population pyramids*. The numbers in each five-year age group are plotted separately, the youngest at the bottom, the eldest at the top, the males on the left and the females on the right:

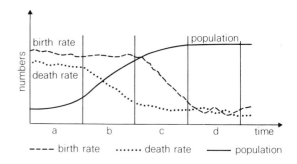

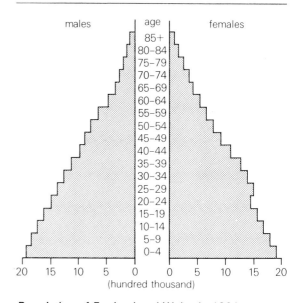

Population of England and Wales in 1901

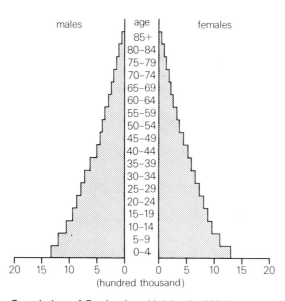

Population of England and Wales in 1851

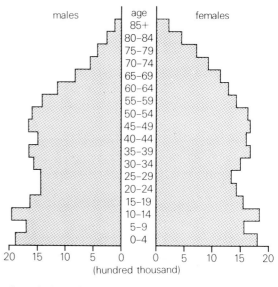

Population of England and Wales in 1951

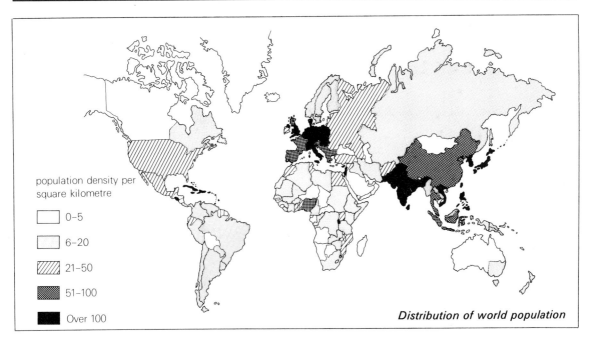

Distribution of world population

Growth rate (% per annum)	Number of years before population doubles
0.5	139
1.0	70
1.5	47
2.0	35
2.5	28
3.0	23
3.5	20

World population growth

At present the world population growth rate is 1.7%; this means that it could double during the next 42 years. Growth rates vary in different parts of the world:

Africa	2.6
Asia	2.3
North America	1.1
South America	2.8
Europe	0.7
USSR	0.9
Oceania	2.0

Study of the above shows that the richer countries have lower growth rates than the poorer ones. The rich countries (which include South Africa and Japan) are called *developed countries* and poor countries are called *developing countries*. There are rich people and poor people in all countries; a rich country is one with a high *gross national product* per head of population (the GNP is the total value of all goods and services produced in a country in a year). The richest countries have a GNP per head of population of over £2500 while the poorest have a GNP per head of population of only £50. Some two-thirds of the world's people are very poor and forty per cent have diets which are deficient in protein.

How can the world which is not adequately feeding its present population hope to feed one twice as big? ...Q.4

Are the rich countries thinly populated and the poor ones densely populated? ...Q.5

Dependents

In all nations there is a proportion of people who have no income and are *dependent* upon others. The largest of these dependent groups are children and old people. Children cost much more than old people, they eat more, need more clothes, require educating and have high expectations. The poorer countries have a larger proportion of dependent children than the richer ones:

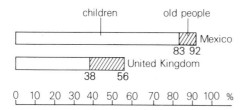

A fall in the birth rate is a big advantage to a country, as it reduces the number of dependents without any immediate reduction in the labour force, thus raising the *per capita income* (i.e., income per head of population) and making the country less poor. A further advantage of a falling birth rate is that in fifteen years or so there is a reduction of the numbers of school leavers seeking employment, relieving the problem of unemployment.

Child–women ratio

The more children and the more women of child-bearing age there are in a population the more likely it is to increase. Demographers calculate a child–woman ratio to determine the likely growth rate:

$$\text{child–woman ratio} = \frac{\text{the number of children aged 0–4}}{\text{the number of women aged 15–49}}$$

The higher this ratio, the larger the expected population growth. In the richer countries it is 0.3 to 0.4, while it is over 0.75 in the poorest nations.

Problems of a rapidly increasing world population

The most obvious problem is producing enough food to meet the extra requirements. It is estimated that in order to double agricultural production the uses of fertilisers and pesticides would have to increase ten times – think about the environmental problems this would cause.

What environmental problem is caused by
(a) fertilisers
(b) pesticides? ...Q.6

Also, many fertilisers and pesticides are made from fossil fuels which are rapidly being used up.

In some parts of the world more land could be brought into agricultural production by clearing forests; this could well upset the oxygen/carbon dioxide balance in the atmosphere as trees account for a large proportion of the world's photo-synthesis. In any case, do we want a world without forests geared entirely to food production?

Problems of water supply and sewage disposal would arise and there would be increased demand for the mineral resources which are already seriously depleted. With all available land being used for food production living space would be scarce and there would be no space for recreation. From any point of view a doubling of the world's population is extremely undesirable and it should be prevented.

Preventing a population explosion

The only humane way to stop rapid population increase is to reduce the birth rate.

In China this is being achieved by encouraging late marriages, birth spacing and a maximum of two children per family. Women are urged not to marry until they are 24 and men until they are 26; after the first child is born they are advised to wait five years before having their second (and final) child. To make this family planning possible, contraceptives, sterilisation and abortion are all free and easily available. In spite of this there are still 33 Chinese children born each minute against 11 people who die. The estimated 1982 population of 1000 million is expected to become 1200 million by the year 2000.

In the UK there is no direct government pressure to limit family size. Couples receive weekly payments for each child which could encourage larger families. Contraceptives are available on National Health prescriptions and abortion is also legal. The main reason for a low birth rate in this country appears to be a desire on the part of parents to give themselves and their children a high standard of living, which is much easier with a small family.

India, with fourteen per cent of the world's population and only two per cent of its land, has been attempting to reduce the birth rate for many years. Women are encouraged to use the loop (a method of contraception which involves inserting a small plastic and copper device into the uterus) and men are encouraged to be sterilised. The Indians have been less successful than the Chinese

in reducing the birth rate. Some governments appear to be unconcerned about population growth and take no action to encourage their people to have less children.

Investigation 8.3

Visit a graveyard with your class and, working in pairs with each pair having its own section, record the following information from each tombstone:

Name	Male or female	Year born	Year died	Age at death	Other information

Back in the classroom make a scattergram with age on the vertical axis and year on death on the horizontal axis (a scattergram is produced in exactly the same way as a graph except that no points are joined as there may be several different values on the vertical axis for each point on the horizontal axis).

Does the pattern of dots on the scattergram show a general trend?

Calculate the average age of death for (a) men and (b) women for each decade.

Can you make any deductions about family size from the information you have collected?

Questions: Population

1. Write single sentences to answer the following questions.
   (a) How long would it take to breed a thousand descendants from a single pair of rabbits?
   (b) What methods are the Chinese using to stem the population increase?
   (c) In what way may the removal of large areas of forest affect the composition of the atmosphere?
   (d) When is the next UK census likely to be held?
   (e) If the annual growth rate of a population is 1.5%, how long will it be before that population doubles?

2. At the last census the population distribution by age and sex of a small town was:

   (a) Construct a population pyramid of the town.
   (b) Comment upon the unusual shape of the pyramid.
   (c) Why is the top of the pyramid skewed to one side?

3. (a) What factors limit the growth of a natural population?
   (b) Why have these factors not stemmed the growth of the world human population?

4. Explain how man can control:
   (a) natality
   (b) mortality

   What effect do these controls have upon changes in the human population?

Age	0–4	5–9	10–14	15–19	20–24	25–29	30–34	35–39	40–44
Female	420	346	408	324	375	437	476	438	491
Male	459	357	398	338	347	443	452	427	507

Age	45–49	50–54	55–59	60–64	65–69	70–74	75–79	80–84	85+
Female	527	642	821	1200	1198	1142	851	426	219
Male	539	611	805	1154	1097	985	661	206	97

9 Land use and the urban environment

The many uses of land

The quality and appearance of the environment depends upon the use or *misuse* man is making of the land. Nearly all man's activities use a certain area of land. Your house is built on land, so is your school, and the road you use to get from one to the other. The food you eat needs land to grow on, the water you drink may have been stored in a reservoir, the rubbish you make has to go somewhere and the paper for your books was grown in the forest.

There are 24 million hectares of land in the UK, of which agriculture uses 19 million hectares.

Other uses are: travel and transport, recreation, manufacturing, waste disposal, quarrying, education, residential, commerce, forestry (see *Rural Science 1*), horticulture, water storage, military training, energy conversion, hospitals, administration.

Task 9.1

Examine the nine photographs below and opposite and write down the land use in each. Turn to page 128 and check your answers.

A

B

C

D

E

F

G

H

I

The land use pattern determines whether an area is countryside, town, suburb or village. In the country agriculture and forestry dominate but there is also a proportion of land used for transport, commerce, housing, education etc. In the town agriculture and forestry are non-existent, open spaces are parks for recreation and trees are grown for their amenity value.

Investigation 9.1

Obtain a large-scale map of the area around your school. Cut the map into sections, one section for every two pupils. Take your section of the map to the area it represents and carefully mark the use to which each part of the area is being put.

Back in the classroom decide upon a common key, such as red for residential land, brown for commerce (shops and offices), blue for factories and so on. Colour your map according to the key. When all the colouring is complete, tape the pieces together to produce a land use map of the area around your school.

- ☒ residential
- ☒ education
- ⊡ recreation
- ⊠ administration
- ⊞ commerce

Towns and conurbations

Most towns in this country were not planned, but grew from settlements where work was available and the nearby countryside had soil and climate to produce enough surplus food to feed the town dwellers. In the 1920s and 1930s cheap buses enabled people to live further from their work and the settlements expanded as houses were built along the roadside – this is known as *ribbon development*.

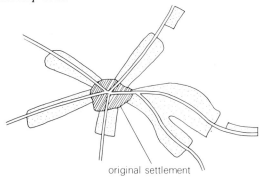

original settlement

Later, the areas between the ribbons were built upon as the town continued to expand outwards. In some areas there were a number of expanding towns. These eventually met, giving rise to a number of towns with no countryside in between; such an area is known as a *conurbation*. In the West Midlands conurbation it is possible to travel through six or more towns without seeing a field. This is also true of many other urban areas.

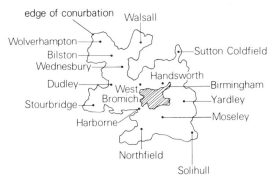

edge of conurbation — Walsall
Wolverhampton
Bilston — Sutton Coldfield
Wednesbury
Handsworth
Dudley — West Bromich — Birmingham
Stourbridge — Yardley
Harborne — Moseley
Northfield
Solihull

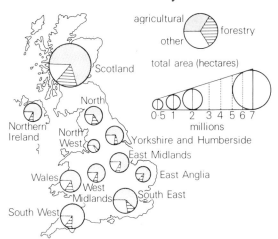

agricultural / forestry / other
total area (hectares)
0·5 1 2 3 4 5 6 7
millions

Scotland
North
Northern Ireland
North West
Yorkshire and Humberside
East Midlands
Wales
East Anglia
West Midlands
South East
South West

Land use in the different U.K. regions

Which region of the UK has the highest proportion of
(a) Forestry? (b) Other? (c) Agriculture?...Q.1

Task 9.2

List as many different land uses as possible which may be included in 'other' in the land use map on page 116.

Demand for land

In 1945 good agricultural land could be purchased for £200 per hectare. In 1982 similar land cost £5000 per hectare and if there was permission to change the use of that land to residential one hectare could cost £250 000. Part of this large increase is due to inflation. Another reason for the increase is that land is a finite resource which is in very great demand; the wealth of the population has increased but the area of land has not. There is only so much land and the area cannot be increased (except for certain small areas of reclamation from the sea e.g. the Yzelmeer in the Netherlands). Land being used for one purpose is not available for another; the land being used for a motorway cannot be used to grow trees. Some land can have two uses; your school field for example may be used for education and recreation.

Change of use

The use to which a certain piece of land is being put can be changed. A rubbish dump can be made into a sports field or a forest can become an airfield. Before land use can be changed permission must be obtained from the planning authority,

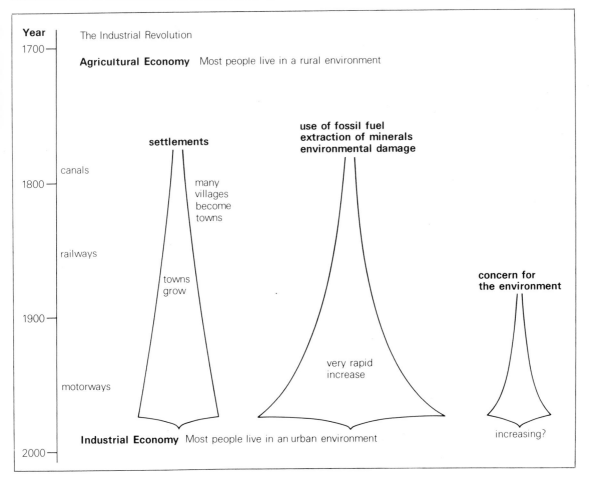

which is usually the local council. (Farmers can erect small farm buildings without planning permission; they can also plant trees instead of wheat and so on, but they cannot change the land to non-agricultural use without planning permission.) If the person applying to change the land use disagrees with the decision of the council he can appeal to the Minister of the Environment who can over-rule the council and decide whether or not the proposed land use change may go ahead.

Investigation 9.2

Village study

1. Obtain an Ordnance Survey map of the village you are to study and from it make an enlarged sketch map showing the lines of communication to the village naming towns and inserting distances:

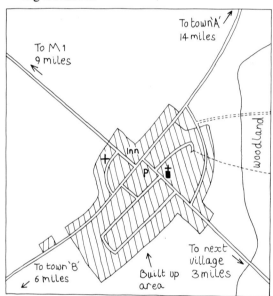

2. Find out as much as you can about the history of the village. For this you will need to do some research – a visit to the nearest public library is essential. Here you may be able to obtain the following:
   (a) A copy of The Doomsday Book (a survey of the lands in England made by William the Conqueror between 1084 and 1086 for the purpose of taxation). If you are fortunate your village will be recorded here.
   (b) Figures from the 1851 census (and more recent ones) which gives the name, age, sex, occupation and birthplace of every individual who was living at that time in the village.

   (c) A book written by a local historian in which there is some information about your village.

   Your teacher may be able to obtain, from the County Archivists Department, a tithe map and schedule; this dates back to 1840.
   The tithe map shows roads, tracks, field boundaries, water courses and the location of buildings, some of which are named in such a way that their usage may be deduced. The schedule is a list of the usage of all plots of land recorded on the tithe map. A tithe was a tax which was payable to the church. Use the information you have obtained to:
   draw a land-use map of the village as it was in 1840.
   draw a line graph showing population change from 1851 to 1981.
   construct population pyramids for 1851 and 1981 and compare them (see page 110).

3. Visit the village and produce a present day land-use map as described on page 116, compare this with the 1840 land-use map.
   Where has the growth (if any) taken place?
   Why has the growth taken place in this area rather than other?

4. List all the services which are available in the village, e.g. Post Office, Butcher, Youth Club.

5. Make a second list of all the services you consider essential for modern living, e.g. bank, school, dentist, shoe shop. From this list cross out all those which appear in the list (4) and write against the remainder where the villagers have to travel for these services.

6. Obtain a bus (and train if there is a station) timetable and examine it carefully.

Are villagers able to use Public transport for travel:

(a) to work if they begin work at 7.00 a.m.? 8.00 a.m.? 9.00 a.m.?

(b) home from work if they finish at 4.00 p.m.? 5.00 p.m.? 6.00 p.m.?

(c) to a nearby town for two hours shopping on any day they wish?

(d) to a place of entertainment in the evening?

(e) to visit a sick person in hospital on a Sunday afternoon?

or are the villagers dependant upon the private car for these and other activities?

Investigation 9.3

Street scape in an urban environment

The street scape (street scene) is made up of many parts including:

(a) buildings;
(b) road surfaces;
(c) pavement surfaces;
(d) signs;
(e) pillars and posts;
(f) walls and fences;
(g) street furniture.

1. Copy this assessment grid into your notebook.

score	very 0	fairly 1	in between 2	fairly 3	very 4	
dirty						clean
ugly						attractive
in need of repair						well maintained

2. Visit the street you are to investigate and look at each of the categories a–g in turn; think about their condition and appearance and record each letter three times in the appropriate box.

e.g. If the buildings were fairly clean, very well maintained and fairly attractive and you also decide that the road surfaces were fairly clean, needing some repair and were neither ugly nor attractive, your grid would look like this:

score	very 0	fairly 1	in between 2	fairly 3	very 4	
dirty				ab		clean
ugly			b	a		attractive
in need of repair		b			a	well maintained

3. Record also whether trees are present and award marks using the scale overleaf:

Both sides tree lined	4
Several trees on each side	3
One or two trees	2
No trees but other greenery visible	1
No greenery visible	0
Total the number of points scored	

Repeat the investigation in another street and compare the results. What do you think could be done to improve the street scape in the street with the lowest score?

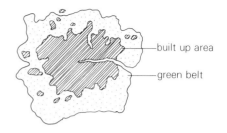

Green belts

A green belt is an area of land around a town or city in which development is not usually allowed. As long ago as 1938 a green belt ten miles wide around London was set up by Act of Parliament.

Green belts around towns prevent one town from joining with another. They also give town dwellers an area of countryside nearby and a different landscape which adds to the quality of life. Some of the green belt areas have been unsuccessful and large residential developments have arisen immediately outside the green belt. In some areas exceptions to green belt regulations have led to their complete loss.

Listed buildings

Many old buildings are considered to be beautiful. Some are very good examples of the architecture of a past age and others are unique due to their historic importance (Shakespeare's birthplace for example). These buildings are 'listed' by the Department of the Environment, which means that they must not be demolished nor their exterior changed as they are an important part of our building heritage which must be preserved for future generations. There are over 15 000 listed buildings in the country.

Dr Samuel Johnson's birthplace

Town trees

Trees can be a very important part of the urban scene. They add interest with their colour change and their natural shapes contrast in a pleasing way with the straight lines of the buildings. Trees can be preserved by making a 'tree preservation order'. When such an order is put on a tree by the local authority it becomes an offence to remove it and even the owner of the tree is not allowed to fell it.

When new areas of countryside are being developed, planners usually try to leave as many mature trees standing as possible. In addition the local authority can give permission for a development to go ahead subject to the developer planting trees to screen the development. Stevenage New Town has more trees than people.

Town planning

Town planners try to improve existing towns by producing a town map showing the different 'zones' as it is and a second map showing the 'zones' as they would like them to be sometime in the future. This town map has to conform to the Department of the Environment's regional plan which shows a land use plan for each area.

The regional plan also covers the rural areas. The development plan for your area may be seen at the council offices.

Which two types of land use are on the old map but not on the new? ...**Q.2**
Which type of land use is on the new map but not on the old? ...**Q.3**

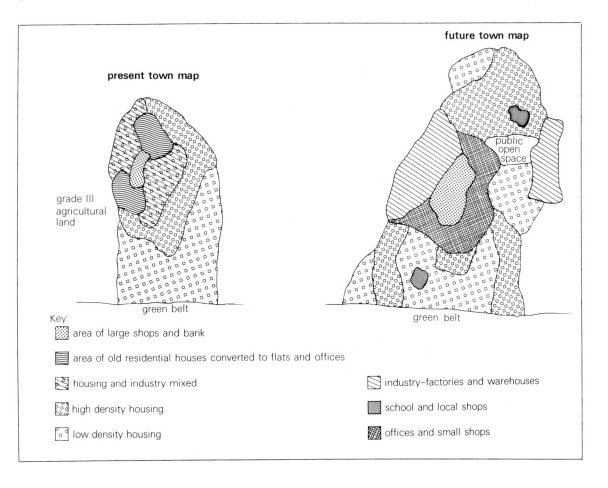

present town map

future town map

grade III agricultural land

public open space

green belt

green belt

Key:
area of large shops and bank

area of old residential houses converted to flats and offices

housing and industry mixed

high density housing

low density housing

industry-factories and warehouses

school and local shops

offices and small shops

Future planning permission is then given only if it complies with the new town map. Planning permission is not only required for new development. It is also necessary for 'change of use'.

An actual town map is usually more complicated than the one shown, but the principles of keeping industry and housing separate and of providing local shopping facilities are fairly general.

What problems could arise by mixing industry and houses? ...Q.4

New homes built within 700 m of town centre

High cost of land, high rates, the zoning of the town map, the availability of motorised transport and several other factors have led to the depopulation of the town centres. For example, those of Birmingham, Bristol, Glasgow, Liverpool, Manchester and Edinburgh become deserted at night, on Sundays and on bank holidays. Some planners believe this to be undesirable and in some areas residences are being built once more near to the town centres.

It is a strange fact that although planners can say no to proposed developments they cannot direct development. For example, if the planners would like a shop in a certain position they cannot have one unless a developer is prepared to build one.

Task 9.3

One method of housing a lot of people on a small area of land is to build high-rise flats instead of houses. Imagine what life would be like in a high-rise flat (or if you live in a high-rise flat imagine what life would be like in a house) and list all the advantages and all the disadvantages you can imagine of replacing a group of old houses with a block of high-rise flats.

New towns

Many of the older urban areas have high-density housing (i.e. over 50 dwellings per hectare) fairly near to the centres, built to house factory workers and their families long before the advent of the omnibus and the private motor car. Much of this housing is substandard and in order to check the growth of the conurbations, the occupants have been (and are still being) rehoused in new towns. The new towns are usually based on existing small towns or villages, although three (Warrington, Peterborough and Northampton) have been based on larger towns. This gives the new towns the advantage of facilities which are already available. Unlike older towns, new towns are planned from the start and make allowances for the motorcar. New towns provide facilities in addition to houses which include shops, banks, hotels, car parks, recreational facilities, open spaces, parks, industrial sites, public houses, schools, churches and so forth on a properly planned basis. Over a million people have moved into the new towns. A new town inevitably means the loss of some rural landscape.

Task 9.4

1. Draw an outline map of the British Isles.
2. Using an atlas, mark in the new towns from the list below:
   Antrim, Aycliffe, Ballymena, Basildon, Bracknell, Central Lancashire New Town, Corby, Craigavon, Crawley, Cumbernauld, Cumbran, East Kilbride, Glenrothes, Harlow, Hatfield, Hemel Hempstead, Irvine, Livingston, Londonderry, Milton Keynes, Newtown, Northampton, Peterborough, Peterlee, Redditch, Runcorn, Skelmersdale, Stevenage, Telford, Warrington, Washington, Welwyn Garden City.

3. Mark in the large cities which you think have lost populations to the new towns.
4. What do you notice about the distribution of the new towns?

Towns *other* than new towns were developed before the motor car was invented. In those days journeys took a long time and consisted of a number of stages from town to town. Consequently most roads went through the centre of the towns. Once motorised transport became available this pattern of roads caused congestion and made journeys unnecessarily slow. Some towns still have a main road through the centre, to the annoyance of both resident and motorist. This problem is being solved in two ways:

1. Bypasses: roads which take traffic around the town instead of through it.
2. Motorways: specially constructed roads which keep traffic away from man's other activities.

In the middle of this century the majority of shopping areas consisted of shop-lined streets through which traffic was flowing:

Shoppers were subject to noise, dirt and fumes in addition to the danger and difficulty of crossing from one side to the road to the other. Planners responded by separating shoppers from traffic with pedestrian-only shopping areas. Purpose-built pedestrian precincts are fairly straight-forward but to pedestrianise an existing high-street shopping area is much more difficult. Not only does the traffic have to be rerouted, but shops must have access at the rear in order to take delivery of goods. In addition to the physical problems many of the traders opposed pedestrian-isation schemes in the belief that if street parking was not available the number of customers would decrease.

Task 9.5

Think about shopping in a pedestrian precinct and compare it with shopping alongside a busy main road. List all the advantages and the disadvantages associated with each area:

1. from the shopper's viewpoint;
2. from the motorist's viewpoint.

Remember: the shopkeeper is also involved in pedestrianisation, but his over-riding concern is the effect it will have on his shop – will it increase or decrease trade?

Traffic flows

There are over 18 million vehicles licensed for use on roads in the UK and 78% of all goods are moved by road (14% by rail and 8% by pipeline). Road traffic makes a very large impact upon the environment especially upon the urban environment where most journeys either begin or end.

Number of lorries licensed in UK, 1946–80 (*thousands*)

	1946	1950	1955	1960	1965	1970	1975	1980
lorries under 1½ tonnes	204	364	534	757	864	933	1107	1150
lorries 1½–8 tonnes	325	481	525	574	614	565	500	423
lorries over 8 tonnes	1	2	5	11	24	55	96	121

Traffic causes noise, fumes, congestion and a big visual impact.

On the other hand railways are much less intrusive and are usually separated from people by buildings or hoardings. Electric trains have the advantage of being pollution free. (It must be remembered that the electricity they use is creating some pollution at the place where it is being generated.)

It is very difficult to find a place in a town where cars or lorries cannot be seen or heard.

Which group of lorries has made the largest percentage increase? ...Q.5
What is the advantage to the lorry owner of having a very large lorry? ...Q.6
What is the advantage to the consumer of transporting goods in a large lorry? ...Q.7
What are the advantages of a large lorry? ...Q.8
Why are a number of smaller lorries often more environmentally acceptable than one large one? ...Q.9

One way of preventing heavy lorries from short cutting through residential streets

Investigation 9.4

The traffic flows around your town

This is a class investigation as a number of counts have to be made in different places at the same time.

1. Make a sketch map showing the nearest town centre (shaded in) with the roads which serve it; mark in also any major road which bypasses the area.

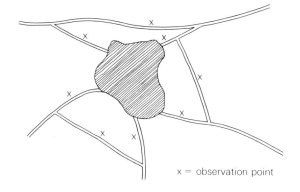

x = observation point

2. Mark on the map a number of observation points from where the traffic could be monitored.

3. At a given time count the traffic on the road, two students at each observation point.

4. Your chart should look like this:

N→S traffic	S→N traffic
JHT JHT JHT III	JHT JHT JHT II

Back in the classroom record the information on the map by drawing circles near the observation points and inserting two arrows in each circle, the thickness of each arrow proportional to the number of vehicles:

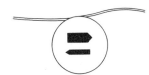

A survey similar to the one above produced the following results:

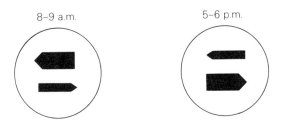

8–9 a.m.   5–6 p.m.

Give a possible explanation of the above traffic flows.

Not all roads are busiest on weekdays. For example, the graph above shows the traffic flow over a whole week on a road leading to a local beauty spot near a town in Wales:

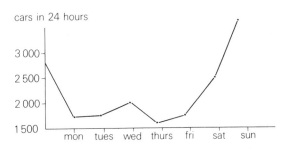

cars in 24 hours

How can the peak on Wednesday be accounted for?
...Q.10

The traffic flow pattern of this same road on a summer Sunday is shown by the graph below:

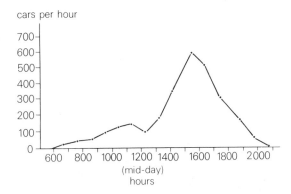

cars per hour

It is also possible to survey the route traffic is taking at a busy junction. To do this one person is stationed on either side of each approach road, then for a set period they write down all the odd registration numbers as each vehicle passes. Each vehicle is thus recorded as it approaches the junction and again as it leaves it. It is easy to determine which routes are being used. After the survey the numbers recorded on each route are doubled to give the actual volume of traffic on each route.

This method is used by the Ministry of Transport and their agents.

Refuse disposal

Urban areas generate a lot of rubbish. It is the duty of the local authority to collect and dispose of household waste and to provide the facilities for the dumping of garden and other refuse (see

photograph overleaf). The District Council collects the waste and the County Council (or Metropolitan Council in conurbations) dispose of it.

Investigation 9.5

During one week, instead of throwing all waste in the dustbin provide seven plastic bags for rubbish from your household.

Label the bags as follows:

1. Tin cans and other metals.
2. Organic matter.
3. Ash.
4. Paper and cardboard.
5. Bottles and glass.
6. Plastics.
7. Other material.

Ask the family to co-operate by placing the rubbish in separate bags. At the end of the week weigh the bags before putting them in the dustbin for collection. Display your finds on a histogram.

Make a list of all the items discarded by your household which:

(a) are biodegradable;
(b) can be recycled.

In many households one of the above bags would always be empty; why is this? ... **Q.11**

Tipping

The local authority has to dispose of the rubbish it collects. The easiest and cheapest method of disposal is to tip the rubbish in a hole in the ground. Almost 80% of the 70 million tonnes of town waste produced in Britain each year is buried in the ground. (See page 115H.)

In some areas there are many holes caused by open-cast mining, quarrying and disused railway cuttings. Each layer of rubbish is capped with a layer of earth; care has to be taken that the tips do not become the breeding ground for rats.

Water leached from a tip can cause ten times more pollution than sewage, and tipping sites over porous rock may be lined with marl to protect the underlying rock.

Why must porous rocks be protected from pollution? ... **Q.12**

The tipping method of refuse disposal can be a useful method of reclaiming land laid waste by industrial activity. Once the hole is filled to the desired level it can be capped with subsoil, followed by a layer of topsoil, and put into use. If the land is to be used for growing trees the layer of soil can be very much thinner than if the reclaimed land is to be used for cropping.

An old railway cutting ... filled with rubbish covered with soil ready for sowing

Dumping waste in holes in the ground, is in itself a wasteful use of resources, especially when so much could be recycled or made into fertiliser. Perhaps future generations will dig up our waste dumps in order to extract useful materials which we just throw away.

In addition to household waste there is the waste from many industrial processes, some of which, is toxic. Any firm which produces toxic waste must inform the County Council who control the dumping. After toxic wastes are dumped council officials inspect the tips at regular intervals to ensure that the materials are still 'safe'.

Incineration

Not all waste is tipped. In some areas there are no convenient tipping sites and the volume of waste is reduced by baling, pulverising or incinerating before being finally tipped. In incineration plants (see photograph above) nine cubic metres of household waste are reduced to one cubic metre of ash for tipping. Incineration has the additional advantage that the final product is sterile, also in some areas, for example Doncaster, use is made of the heat generated while the rubbish burns.

Recycling

In the plant photographed above the ferrous metals (mostly iron) are removed from the ash by means of an electro-magnet. The metal is baled and the bales sent to a plant for recycling.

Another waste product which is easily recycled is paper. However, in many areas no attempt is made to separate paper from the other rubbish and it gets dumped or burnt. This is a pity, as every tonne of paper recycled saves two trees from being cut down. The cost of sorting the collected rubbish (or making separate collections from households where paper has been placed in different containers from other rubbish) is often greater than the value of the scrap paper. Pulp made from scrap paper containing printer's ink makes paper of lower quality than new pulp. Almost all the cardboard manufactured in the UK is made from recycled paper.

Task 9.6

Tear up about 5 g of newspaper into pieces about 250 mm square. Place it in a liquidiser with 500 ml of water. Run the liquidiser for 60 to 90 seconds to disperse the fibres throughout the water; this mixture is called *slurry*.

Put a wet filter paper into a Buchner funnel and half fill with diluted slurry (one part slurry, three parts water). Draw the water from the funnel with an air pump. Hold the funnel upside down over a smooth surface (glass or plastic laminate) and blow out the contents. Remove surplus water by pressing firmly with a paper towel and leave to dry. Then peel the paper you have recycled from the filter paper and compare it with the original newspaper.

Urban wildlife

From the ground an urban area appears to be a mass of roads and buildings which would not support any wildlife; however, from the air the appearance is quite different; gardens, parks, street trees, public open spaces, derelict sites, canal banks and churchyards produce a wealth of vegetation which together with organic waste supports a surprisingly large number of species. Buildings give homes to many wild animals and birds, which find their living without ever visiting the country. A group of surburban houses with established gardens forms a much better habitat for birds than any large cornfield, with its single plant species and absence of nesting sites.

Even large animals like the fox live and breed in towns. Bristol, for example, has a population of over 500 foxes living in cellars and under garden sheds by day and feeding at night on worms, voles, mice and small birds in addition to raiding waste bins and bird tables and being fed by animal lovers.

Answers to Task 9.1

A: recreation (allotments); B: use being changed to residential; C: mining, residential, industrial, agricultural; D: recreational, agricultural out of season; E: forestry, recreational; F: agricultural; G: industrial, transport, recreational (canal); H: rubbish tip; I: transport, urban amenities.

Questions: Land use and the urban environment

1. Write single sentences to answer the following questions.
    (a) What is a green belt?
    (b) During which years was the Doomsday Book compiled?
    (c) Which group of people may erect small buildings without planning permission?
    (d) For which purposes is land in towns unlikely to be used?
    (e) For what reasons are trees planted in the streets?
    (f) Where may the development plan for your area be seen?
    (g) What percentage of goods are moved by road in the UK?
    (h) Give an example of a common material which is non-biodegradeable.

2. (a) What are the environmental advantages and disadvantages of moving goods by rail?
    (b) At present only 14% of goods moved in the UK go by rail. What benefits (if any) would an increase in this percentage have upon the environment?

3. (a) Describe how the rubbish collected from your home each week is disposed of.
    (b) In what ways could the disposal of this rubbish be
        (i) less wasteful?
        (ii) more environmentally acceptable?

4. (a) List *five* factors which make up a townscape.
    (b) Take each factor in turn and say how it may (i) enhance and (ii) degrade the scene.

5. (a) Describe the historical development of a village you have studied.
    (b) In what ways has the introduction of motorised transport influenced the more recent developments?

10 Conservation

The meaning of conservation

Conservation is not an easy word to understand. Its meaning varies a little according to what is being conserved. The dictionary may say 'preservation of the natural environment', but this definition fails to mention urban conservation, and it also raises the question, 'What is the natural environment?' We know that the entire 'natural environment' in this country has been changed by man. We also know that nature changes an environment and if left a field will become a forest. Conservation must not mean keeping things exactly as they are, since they are not perfect. Conservation must allow for change and improvement, for example a landscape can be less pleasing if it suffers the loss of some hedgerows, together with the hedgerow trees; on the other hand, clear felling of part of a pine forest can enhance the landscape, especially if the area removed is irregular and gets replaced with trees of a different species to give a contrast and relieve a large patch of very dark green.

When applied to fossil fuels conservation has a different meaning. It does not mean that we must suddenly stop using them, as those we do use will not be replaced. Conservation means using them as economically as possible and on no account wasting any. Conservation of raw materials involves the maximum amount of recycling.

Conservation of a species is straightforward and means preventing the decline in a population of plants or animals; this is usually done best by maintaining the habitat necessary for its success. The conservation of an old breed of farm animal or old variety of vegetable can only be achieved as a deliberate effort by man for without him they would very soon be extinct.

Part of the 1982 Wildlife and Countryside Act was aimed at protecting species. The main points from this section of the act are:

1. You must not kill, injure, take or sell any specially protected wild animal e.g. bat, otter, badger, red squirrel (this is not the complete list).
2. You must not disturb specially protected animals in their places of shelter.
3. All wild birds, their nests and eggs are protected (except a few pest and sporting species).
4. There are very harsh penalties for harming certain rare species of birds.
5. Uprooting any wild plant is illegal.
6. Picking or selling certain specially protected wild plants is illegal.

Conservation means caring for and developing for a modern need without destroying.

With the exception of the Netherlands, the United Kingdom is the most densely populated country in Europe; each person has only some 4000 m² of land. This small area (half the size of a rugby pitch) must provide living space, industrial space, recreational space and space to grow food. Much of our space is overseas as we each use quite a large area of the world outside the UK to grow our food. It is important, therefore, that every individual in this country (including you) is conservation conscious.

Conservation bodies

A conservation body is an organisation or a group of people who try to conserve some part of the environment. It could be a small group of local people trying to prevent the closure of a nearby footpath or it could be a large organisation intent on conserving hundreds of kilometres of coastline.

Statutory bodies

These are bodies concerned with conservation which are set up by Parliament and financed from general taxation.

The Countryside Commission and Nature Conservancy Council are advisory bodies. In addition, the Forestry Commission and the Department of the Environment are involved in conservation.

The metropolitan councils, county councils, district councils and parish councils may (or may not) be involved according to the wishes of their members.

Voluntary bodies

These are bodies set up by interested and concerned groups of people and funded by voluntary subscriptions.

Examples of voluntary bodies are the National Trust; the Council for the Protection of Rural England; the Friends of the Earth; the Royal Society for Nature Conservation and the local Trusts (there is one in your area); the Historic Buildings Society; the Heritage Group; the Ramblers' Association; the World Wildlife Fund; the Royal Society for the Protection of Birds; the Rare Breeds Trust; there are many more.

The work of the various bodies is coordinated by The Committee for Environmental Conservation (Co-En-Co).

Countryside Commission

The Countryside Commission was set up by the government in 1968 to keep under review the following areas of public interest:

1. The provision and improvement of facilities for the enjoyment of the countryside.
2. The conservation and enhancement of the natural beauty and amenity of the countryside.
3. The need to secure public access to the countryside for the purposes of open-air recreation.
   There is a similar body in Scotland.

The Countryside Commission designated ten areas as National Parks and a number of smaller areas as 'Areas of Outstanding Natural Beauty' (AONB), some of which offer opportunities for open-air recreation.

Each year, the Countryside Commission is allocated a sum of money from general taxation to run its organization and to distribute to local authorities and other people to either improve the landscape or provide facilities which help people to enjoy the countryside.

The Countryside Commission also provides suggestions to protect certain coasts to establish country Parks, picnic sites and long distance footpaths.

Task 10.1

The areas on the map lettered A–J are the national parks, those lettered V–Z are forest parks and the numbers 1–8 are long distance footpaths.

The national parks are the North York Moors; Dartmoor; the Brecon Beacons; the Peak District; the Pembrokeshire Coast; Exmoor; the Lake District; Snowdonia; Northumberland; the Yorkshire Dales. The forest parks are Aberfoyle; Borders; Arrochar; Galloway; Glenmore.

The Long Distance Footpaths are the Ridgeway Path; the Pennine Way; the South Downs Way; the South West Peninsular Coast Path; Offa's Dyke Path; the Cleveland Way; the Pembrokeshire Coast path; the North Downs Way.

Pair the letters with the correct national and forest parks and the numbers with the correct long distance footpaths. Turn to page 141 and check your answers.

National parks

A National Park is an extensive area of natural beauty to be preserved and improved for the enjoyment of the public.

As in other parts of the country most of the land in national parks is privately owned; there are more restrictions upon building and change of use of land in national parks than in other areas. The Lake District and the Peak District have special planning boards but plans in the other eight are vetted by the local authority.

You may have noticed that in some national parks the telephone kiosks are painted grey instead of the usual red. Why is this? ...Q.1

The Countryside Commission may give 75% of the cost of developing facilities for public access (car parks, stiles etc.) and there is also money available to assist with the establishment of hotels from the English Tourist Board.

The Countryside Commission has drawn up a code of conduct for visitors known as the *Country Code*, which is:

1. Keep to the paths across farmland.
2. Fasten all gates.
3. Avoid fires.
4. Leave no litter – take it home.
5. Safeguard water supplies.
6. Go carefully on country roads.
7. Keep dogs under control.
8. Avoid damaging walls and fences.
9. Protect wildlife.
10. Respect the life of the countryside.

Task 10.2

1. Learn the Country Code by heart.
2. Write two or three sentences about each point in the Country Code to say why you think it was included.

Honeypot areas

Large areas of land in the national parks are not available for the visiting public, as they are privately owned. Visitors tend to concentrate in certain areas, where they can walk or sit in their cars to enjoy the views. They also visit other areas where they can buy refreshments. At peak times these places are quickly filled and parking becomes difficult. Such areas are known as *honeypot areas*.

In addition to visiting national parks to enjoy the views and the countryside air, many visit for special pursuits – camping, climbing, orienteering and so on. The honeypot areas and the areas where certain activities can take place become over used, and trampling and parking begin to change the character of the area.

Country parks

In order to reduce the pressure on the national parks and also to make accessible some country areas nearer to certain large cities, the county councils are empowered (under the Countryside Act 1968) to establish country parks. Country parks are areas of the countryside where the public have access for recreational purposes. Provisions like car parks and a warden service are provided

by the county councils and 75% of the cost may be met by the Countryside Commission; the rest comes from the rates.

Most country parks are small and often consist of car parks near a lake or view. Sometimes a country park is an area of special interest for nature conservation, and the area is managed to allow access and to conserve the natural flora and fauna. If a country park was badly managed then valuable habitats could easily be destroyed and the area could lose much of its recreational value.

A badly managed park would not be as pleasant for the visitor, for example if noise from model aeroplane enthusiasts became a source of annoyance the park managers could restrict this activity to one particular area, or to certain times or even ban it altogether. That would be a management decision; the next task will give you more insight into the role of the managers of a country park.

Task 10.3

Listed below are thirteen management problems that occurred in a country park followed by thirteen possible solutions. Read the problems and solutions, think carefully about them, and pair the problem with the correct solution.

When you have *finished* turn to the end of the book and check your answers.

Management problems

1. Cars using forest roads and taking people into an area where young trees were being established.
2. Walks destroying rare marsh plants by trampling.
3. Horses being ridden through a site of special scientific interest (SSSI) destroying a rare plant species.
4. Numbers of fallow deer raiding fields and gardens for food.
5. A pine forest was unsightly from the road; also the piles of dry needles were a fire risk.
6. Roadside parking causing traffic hazard.
7. Some vandalism around a honeypot area.
8. Some SSSIs suffering damage through trampling.

9. Campers causing damage in several areas.
10. Two areas getting very badly trampled due to heavy usage.
11. Some grass car parks damaged through overuse.
12. Baby deer being worried by dogs.
13. Cars speeding on a forest track being used for access to an ancient monument.

Possible solutions

A. Create a motorless zone.
B. Close thirty per cent of the car parking area to vehicles to allow for rotational use.

C. Erect locking turnpikes at the ends of forest roads.

D. Build a number of ramps across the track.

E. Remove two rows of pines and plant birches in their place.

F. Lay a duckboard path across the wet areas.

G. Improve the warden service.

H. Create deer lawns by adding fertilisers to natural grass and or fertilise the grass on selected firebreaks; also improve browsing by brashing young scrub.

I. Provide a camping area, complete with toilets and other facilities, in one area and ban camping anywhere else.

J. Dig anti-parking ditches along the roadside in vulnerable areas.

K. Re-route the bridle path.

L. Reduce the size of car parks in two areas and extend them in others.

M. Pass a by-law requiring people to keep their dogs on leads in the area where the hinds spend the summer.

The Nature Conservancy Council

This statutory body was set up by Royal Charter in 1949 to:

1. Maintain national nature reserves.
2. Compile lists of sites of special scientific interest (SSSIs).
3. Advise local authorities on nature conservation.
4. Operate six research stations in which scientists work upon conservation problems.

Nature reserves

National nature reserves are representative areas with their natural vegetation and the associated animal species. A national nature reserve protects a habitat and not just a single species. Examples:

Withypool Common, Exmoor – open moorland

Some are owned by the Nature Conservancy Council others managed by them with the consent of the owner. The public may or may not be allowed access to a national nature reserve.

Parsonage Down, Wiltshire – chalk down

Holkham, Norfolk – still water

Nature trails

A nature trail is usually a fairly short walk marked by coloured posts or some other means through an area of countryside. An explanatory leaflet is often available. They may be set up by the Forestry Commission, a local authority, an electricity board, many schools, field study centres or other bodies. Nature trails help to educate and interest people in the countryside; they also concentrate people in particular areas of the countryside leaving other (perhaps more important) areas with less disturbance. Educational nature trails allow many children to pass near, and study, a place of interest without destroying it.

Sites of special scientific interest (SSSI)

These sites may be large or very small. They may contain rare species of plant or animal or they may give a good example of a certain habitat, or they may be of special geological interest. They are chosen by the Nature Conservancy Council and notified to the local planning authority. The local planners must by law inform the Nature Conservancy Council before any plans are passed which would affect an SSSI. If a proposed agricultural improvement is likely to damage an SSSI (e.g. draining an area of marsh or ploughing an area of moorland) the farmer may be compensated for not proceeding with the improvement.

The National Trust

The National Trust is the most important voluntary body. It began in 1895 to preserve places of natural beauty and historic interest. The National Trust (together with the National Trust for Scotland) owns over 200 fine houses with beautiful gardens, the positions of which are marked by the letters NT on Ordnance Survey maps. Although the National Trust depends upon public subscriptions to maintain its properties none of them may be destroyed, sold or built upon without the government's permission.

More recently the National Trust has taken an interest in preserving unspoilt areas of coastline. A fund called 'Enterprise Neptune' was set up which quickly raised over £3,000,000 and over 700 km of coastline is now preserved by the Trust.

The National Trust also run 'Acorn Camps' where young people can go and assist with a conservation project.

The Civic Trust

Unlike the bodies mentioned so far, the Civic Trust is interested in urban rather than rural conservation. It endeavours to preserve buildings of distinction and historic interest, to stimulate interest in the appearance in both town and country, and to inspire a sense of civic pride.

Investigation 10.1

Find a feature which is being conserved in your area. Why is the feature being conserved? Who is conserving it? How is the conservation being paid for?

Do *you* agree with conservation? Give reasons for your answer.

Conservation of specific habitats

The very best method of conserving the large variety of plants and animals in this country is to maintain their habitats; if the habitat is lost then the species cannot survive.

Conservation of heathland

The heathland in the photograph (on the next page) is being invaded by birches and pines as the natural succession is turning the area to woodland. In the Country Park where this photograph was taken, this was the only example of an area of open heathland and the managers wished to retain it. In order to preserve this heathland, volunteers from the local County Naturalists' Trust cut down and removed the pines and birch trees.

Heathland soils are acidic and low in nutrients. Heather, bilberry and crowberry are low-growing shrubby plants which provide food for deer and birds when the plants are young. Regrowth is encouraged by burning or cutting or both. Other plant species found on heathland are heath bed-

Heathland

straw, bracken, purple moor grass and wavey hair grass. Heathland is an important habitat for the whinchat, the grasshopper warbler and the nightjar, a bird which is becoming increasingly rare.

Many insects and spiders have niches in the heathland, including the green hairstreak butterfly and the emperor moth.

Bracken control

The bracken in the photograph opposite is a constant danger to the heathland. With its deep rhizomes and tall dense fronds it overshadows the heather, which dies out in areas where soil is deep enough to support bracken. Bracken has very little associated wildlife and if allowed to grow unchecked would change the character of the area and many valuable habitats would be lost. In order to conserve the heathlands in their present form the managers in this Country Park cut some areas of bracken twice a year which should clear them in about six years' time. In other parks with a similar problem other methods are used:

Rolling. This is done in spring when the young fronds first appear; at this time of year they are brittle and are broken by the roller.

Spraying. Asulox is a selective herbicide which kills bracken without harming other plants and is being used in some parks where the terrain makes other methods impossible.

There is no wish to remove all the bracken, as a reasonable amount adds interest and colour to the landscape and gives physical shelter to certain ground-nesting birds. Too much bracken reduces the availability of important food plants for deer, birds and insects and it is a considerable fire risk.

Conservation of grassland

Natural acid grassland develops on very poor soils and in order to maintain these areas there must be no improvement in the soils, for example by the addition of fertilisers. There are two exceptions to this rule: one is where deer lawns are required and the other is where grassland is to be used for car parking. Other species of more nutritious and hardwearing grasses will grow if fertiliser is applied but the seeds have to be sown.

When deciding which grassland areas are to be enriched with nutrients great care has to be taken that any leaching will not take the chemicals to wetland or other areas (see Eutrophication, page 100).

Conservation of wetlands

Conservation of wetlands is of increasing concern, as very large areas have been lost through agricultural drainage schemes lowering the water table. At time of writing, a whole area of marshland by the Norfolk Broads is threatened by a large drainage scheme which is being opposed by the Council for the Protection of Rural England.

Conservation of landscape

During the last three decades modern agriculture has impoverished parts of the landscape by removing thousands of miles of hedgerows, together with hedgerow trees, to make fields large enough to accommodate the huge machines used for cereal production. The hedges which do remain are unlikely to produce any new trees as the modern hedge trimming machines remove the tops of saplings along with the hedge growth. Some interested farmers allow conservation groups to tag new saplings with strips of bright plastic, these enable the hedgecutter to see the saplings which he can then avoid and leave to grow into new hedgerow trees.

The big tips which mining and industry have scattered over the country have a large and usually detrimental effect upon the landscape. The two photographs above show the effect of the removal of a tip, as they were both taken from the same spot before and after its removal.

The tip was on the north west of the Potteries and the material was so acid that no vegetation could grow upon it. It was removed by Staffordshire County Council at a cost of £166 000, some of which was paid by the Department of the Environment. The task involved removing 230 000 m^3 of material and adding 2000 tonnes of lime, 14.5 tonnes of phosphate fertiliser and 650 kilos of seeds. To complete the work, 20 standard trees and 5000 forest trees were planted.

Conservation of woodland

As oak forest is our natural climax vegetation, it should regenerate itself without the assistance of man. This is not so and most woodlands do not regenerate themselves. Such woodland is designated by the Nature Conservancy Council as *ancient woodland*. There is very little of it, as most woodland has been planted and is harvested and may, or may not, be replanted.

How could you tell whether a woodland was regenerating itself? ... Q.2

Where there is no regeneration, due perhaps to squirrels, rabbits, voles or mice eating either the seeds or the seedlings, conservation bodies could collect seeds from the trees and grow them in a nursery for planting out at a later date in areas of open canopy to replace the older trees when they eventually die.

Dead branches and trees should not be removed but allowed to decay where they have fallen. This will create new niches and habitats as well as allowing the minerals the wood contains to return to the soil.

Investigation 10.2

Ideally this investigation should be carried out in a deciduous wood; if that is not possible the school garden is a good substitute.

During the autumn collect tree seeds in a deciduous wood, keeping the species separate. Mix the seeds with moist sand and store either outside in boxes, where rainfall will keep the sand moist, or in the refrigerator at 4 °C.

The following spring return to the wood, select a suitable area and clear three areas each about half a metre square and sow twelve seeds in each (say three of each of four species). Leave one square unprotected, cover one square with a cage of chicken netting of 50 mm mesh and cover the third square with a cage of fine mesh 5 mm or so (the cages must be sunk into the soil to prevent small rodents from scratching underneath).

Visit the cages at intervals throughout the summer and keep records.

Answer the following questions:

Which tree species are producing viable seeds?

What size animal (if any) is eating tree seeds in spring?

What size animal (if any) is eating tree seedlings?

Which of the four species produced the most seedlings?

Answer also the question:

Is the woodland likely to regenerate itself and if so which species are most likely to dominate?

Conflicts of interest

Conservation very often conflicts with other human activities. For example, a person who wishes to walk quietly in the countryside would not approve of gravel being quarried near his favourite walks, as the noise, dust and general disturbance would spoil his quiet enjoyment. However, that same person would probably approve of the road (built from gravel) which carried his car to the countryside and to the concrete (70% gravel) foundations of his house. Another person may object to the tipping of colliery waste on an area near his home yet would not be without the electricity the coal produces.

With most human activity there are conflicts of interest which have to be solved by compromise; perhaps the ideal solution to the two examples just given would be to use the space from which the gravel was quarried to tip the colliery waste, cap it with soil, and plant vegetation to recreate the lost habitat.

Task 10.4

There are nine objectives different people have for an area of forest and grazing land near to the Yorkshire moors upon which it is hoped to establish a country park.

Copy out the matrix opposite. Decide which objectives conflict a little, and put an 'X' in the box which joins them. Where there is a major conflict between two objectives put a 'C' in the box which joins them.

Individual conservation

Each individual can assist in conservation. Here are a few ideas you may wish to try.

1. Know (and obey) the Country Code.
2. Never waste water.
3. Do not use aerosols – there are alternatives.
4. Limit the use of pesticides.
5. Never drop litter. Take your litter home.

6. If you have a vegetable garden, leave the weeds which grow after harvest to seed – they provide valuable food for wildlife.
7. Leave a small area of lawn uncut and allow a small area of your garden to grow wild – it will produce a variety of interesting plants which will provide food for birds and insects.
8. Do not have a bonfire; recycle lawn cuttings and other vegetable matter by composting and take other items to the authorised tip.
9. Save newspapers and magazines for local groups who may be collecting them.
10. If you have a small patch of nettles, do not destroy it as they provide food for the red admiral, the small tortoiseshell and the peacock butterfly larvae. Cut parts of the clump two or three times during the year to provide a continual supply of young foliage.
11. If you feed birds in winter do not stop until their natural food is available; do not continue too long as some birdtable foods can harm nestlings.
12. If you find a baby bird on the ground leave it

	Extract water from underlying aquifer	Quarry a mineral ore	Commercial production of timber	Protect plant and animal species	Maintain the present landscape	Cater for a wide range of recreational activities	Quiet enjoyment of the countryside	Free public access
Extract water from underlying aquifer								
Quarry a mineral ore								
Commercial production of timber								
Protect plant and animal species								
Maintain the present landscape								
Cater for a wide range of recreational activities								
Quiet enjoyment of the countryside								
Free public access								

alone – the parents are probably feeding it although you will not see them.

13. Make regular use of a bottle bank.
14. Join your local Trust for Nature Conservation (Junior Branch: Watch). Details from the Royal Society for Nature Conservation, 22 The Green, Nettleham, Lincs. (include s.a.e.)
15. Be aware of the need for conservation all the time. Remember, man has already destroyed much of the countryside and he will destroy it all if *you* don't look out!

Very often, conservation can be achieved by very small actions and at very little cost – it just requires a conservation awareness.

For example, cattle grids form traps into which hedgehogs fall and from which they cannot escape and the poor creatures stay there until they die. This problem could easily be overcome either by the inclusion of a small ramp or by fitting a larger drainage pipe.

Modern bridges could easily have ledges incorporated in their design upon which birds could nest.

Unharvested brassicas (see above) can be left to flower if the ground is not required immediately; this provides food for bees and butterflies and later seeds for sparrows and finches.

Questions: Conservation

1. Write single sentences to answer the following questions.
   (a) What is conservation?
   (b) What type of plants grow in abundance on heathland?
   (c) Is the National Trust a statutory body or a voluntary body?
   (d) What do the initials SSSI stand for?
   (e) When visiting the countryside what should you do with your litter?
   (f) Why are many of our wetland environments in danger of being lost?
   (g) Name *five* mammals which may prevent a woodland from regenerating.
   (h) How can you aid conservation in your area?

2. (a) What do you understand by conservation?
   (b) Name *one* feature which is being conserved in your area.
   (c) What steps are being take to achieve this conservation and who is taking them?
   (d) Do you agree with the need to conserve this feature? Give a reason for your answer.

3. (i) What biological effects are human activities having upon a natural environment in your area?
   (ii) What measures could be taken to reverse *two* of these effects?

4. (a) Describe how a heathland may be protected from being destroyed by
      (i) invading bracken
      (ii) invading trees.
   (b) Name *two* insects and *two* birds which are dependant upon the heathland.

5. (a) Name *five* voluntary bodies which operate to conserve aspects of the environment.
   (b) Give *two* examples where conservation bodies may find themselves in conflict with other land users.

Answers to Task 10.1

A: Northumberland; B: Lake District; C: Yorkshire Dales; D: North York Moors; E: Peak District; F: Snowdonia; G: Brecon Beacons; H: Pembrokeshire Coast; I: Exmoor; J: Dartmoor; V: Borders; W: Galloway; X: Aberfoyle; Y: Arrochar; Z: Glenmore.
1: South Downs Way; 2. North Downs Way; 3: Ridgeway Path; 4: South West Peninsular Coast Path; 5: Pembrokeshire Coast path; 6: Offa's Dyke Path: 7: Pennine Way; 8: Cleveland Way.

Answers to in-text questions

1. The world in space

1. Nitrogen 78%; oxygen 21%; other gases 1% including carbon dioxide 03%.
2. Every fourth year the extra quarter days add up to one whole day, i.e. 29 February.
3. The sun rises in the east, this means we must be travelling towards the east.
4. 21 March and 23 September.
5. The sun will be directly overhead at places along the tropic of Capricorn at midday 22 December.
6. There will be no period of daylight north of the Arctic Circle on 22 December.
7. The moon does not rotate, only one side of the moon faces the earth.

2. Rocks and minerals

1. Igneous. 3. Cornwall.
2. Coal. 4. 100 metres.
5. All depend upon iron. Some like railways have a very large iron content, concrete buildings are reinforced with iron, plastics are moulded in steel moulds, joinery depends upon iron nails, screws and tools, and wheat is sown and harvested by machinery which is built from iron.

3. Water

1. More water, as water is necessary to grow the food eaten by the animal.
2. Pipe 'A' is taking water away from the boiler.
3. Hydrogen collects above the negative electrode.
4. Hydrogen has the larger volume (twice the volume of oxygen).
5. The volume of water will be reduced.
6. Clay on one filter paper, nothing on the other.
7. The clay has settled on the bottom, the copper sulphate is still evenly dispersed through the liquid.
8. Copper sulphate, as a white powder.
9. Warm water holds more salt than cold water.
10. Warm water holds less oxygen than cold water.
11. Hard water needs to be softened to save soap, to prevent scale forming inside boilers which would waste fuel, to prevent the bore of pipes from becoming restricted.
12. The scale inside a kettle arises from temporary hard water.
13. 42 joules.
14. 672 joules.
15. The atmospheric pressure is low, this will reduce the temperature at which water boils. A temperature of 100 °C is needed to make a good cup of tea.
16. Water reaches its maximum density at 4 °C.
17. The top layer is 0 °C, the middle layer is 2 °C and the bottom layer is 4 °C.
18. 3037 joules.
19. Transpiring leaves will be cooler due to loss of heat to the evaporating water.
20. The energy from the sun (solar energy) drives the hydrological cycle.
21. The top of the artesian well is higher than the water table.
22. The layer of impervious rock prevents the rain falling on area B from recharging the aquifer.
23. The volume of water which could be pumped from the wells without affecting the volume of the lake would be equal to the rainfall in the recharge area less any lost by evaporation and transpiration.

24. (a) the layer of dirt cleans by physical means. means.
    (b) the layer containing algae cleans by chemical and biological means.
    (c) the layer containing algae and the layer containing bacteria clean by biological means.
25. The amount will vary with the place of collection.

4. The biosphere

1. (a) The weasel is at trophic level 4.
   (b) the weasel is at trophic level 3.
2. In chain A 1000 joules are available to man, while in chain B only 100 joules are available.
3. Grassland – the sheep would prevent trees and and shrubs from becoming established by eating the seedlings and young shoots. Some shrubs like gorse which is very prickly may become established. This is an example of deflected succession.
4. Inside the wood one would expect to find a smaller temperature range, less rainfall, lower windspeeds, higher humidity and less light.
5. Measurements (a) and (b) would be taken and also the height of the plant above the line.
6. More aphids as they provide food for ladybirds.
7. The day–night temperature range will be smaller in the water.
8. The increase in temperature will induce an algal bloom.
9. The most likely substance in the farm ditch which would cause a change in the ecosystem would be nitrogen salts (fertiliser leached from fields). The ditch could also contain some pesticides and herbicides which have been sprayed upon the fields.

5. Food

1. (a) Butter – trophic level 3.
   (b) Margarine – trophic level 2 (assuming the margarine is manufactured entirely from plant oils).
2. The foetus requires protein to grow.

3. They are all derived from animals.
4. Tiny fragments of rock, water, mineral salts, air, humus and bacteria.
5. Method 4.
6. Blackberries, pigeons, rabbits, mushrooms and several others.
7. Method 4 will support most people.
8. Method 1 will support the least number of people.
9. Potatoes will be grown in year 6.
10. Energy flow 1 will give man the largest proportion of the sun's energy.
11. Energy flow 2 will give man the largest amount of protein.
12. (a) Chain 1 – man is at trophic level 2.
    (b) Chain 2 – man is at trophic level 3.
13. This question is impossible to answer as many considerations are necessary. In theory if energy only were necessary for man's health, possibly ten times the number of people could be supported by food chain 1 than by food chain 2. How efficient the cattle were at converting food would also make a difference to the answer.
14. Chemicals have to be tested and approved to protect the health of the nation.
15. If not properly thawed the centre of a chicken may not become hot enough during cooking to kill any harmful organisms that may be present, although the outside of the bird is browned and appears cooked.

6. Energy

1. $1\,000\,000$ (or 1×10^6) joules in a megajoule.
2. 8 kW h.
3. Chemical energy.
4. Walking to school – except that the food you ate, to give you the energy to walk, required fossil fuel to produce it.
5. Less energy as much would be used by the pig.
6. 332 million tonnes of coal.
7. Availability and price of fuels vary, sometimes due to political events and sometimes due to economic reasons.
8. Coal is used to manufacture electricity.
9. Electric trains, electric cars (milk floats etc.).

7. Pollution

1. 21 pollutants are listed.
2. 4 gases, sulphur dioxide, carbon dioxide, carbon monoxide, aerosols (Freon gas).
3. Noise, atomic radiation and heat.
4. Smoke could have the effect of reducing temperature by preventing some solar radiation from reaching the ground.
5. Royal Society for the Protection of Birds.
6. The water which is drawn in the morning will have stood in the pipes overnight; water drawn later in the day will have spent less time in the pipes.
7. Copper and polythene.
8. After 1950 there was very little weed growing upon which snails depend for food.
9. ½ gram.
10. Radioactive waste is continually produced by the nuclear power stations so the amounts involved are increasing.
11. Ozone reduction would increase the amount of ultraviolet radiation reaching the land and life would be destroyed.

8. Population

1. One seed.
2. Cows live for several years and one female may produce ten calves during her lifetime.
3. (a) The total population increases if birth rate rate exceeds death rate.
   (b) The total population decreases if death rate exceeds birth rate.
   (c) The total population is static if birth rate is equal to death rate.
4. Unfortunately there is no answer to this question.
5. No, there is no relationship between wealth and population density.
6. (a) Eutrophication.
   (b) Pesticides enter the biosphere and become concentrated along the food chain.

9. Land use and the urban environment

1. (a) Scotland.
   (b) South East.
   (c) East Midlands.
2. Housing and industry mixed, old residential houses converted to flats and offices.
3. School and local shops, offices and small shops.
4. Residents could be troubled by noise, air pollution and extra traffic, particularly lorries.
5. Lorries over eight tonnes.
6. One driver can move many more goods in a large lorry than he can in a small lorry.
7. The cost of transport will be less, therefore the price the consumer has to pay should be less.
8. The large lorry carries goods at a smaller cost per unit than the small lorry (providing of course that the vehicle is fully loaded).
9. All lorries make noise and fumes, but small lorries cause very much less vibration than large ones. Small lorries have less visual impact and make a much smaller intrusion into the street scene than large lorries.
10. Wednesday is half-day closing in a nearby town and shop workers are visiting the beauty spot.
11. Many households do not use solid fuel and would have no ash to dispose of.
12. Porous rocks hold water which may eventually flow into a water course, or may be extracted for man's use.

10. Conservation

1. Grey is a less intrusive colour than red.
2. In an oak woodland which is regenerating itself there would be oaks of different ages including seedlings and saplings.

Answers to Task 10.3

1C, 2F, 3K, 4H, 5E, 6J, 7G, 8A, 9I, 10L, 11B, 12M, 13D.

Glossary

Abcission layer Layer of cork which seals the spot from which a leaf falls.

Abortion The premature termination of a pregnancy by unnatural means.

Acid rain Rain which is acidic due to pollution with sulphur gases.

Aerosol Container of substance under pressure which is released as a fine spray.

Algae Simple plants which float in water or live in damp places.

Algal bloom Very rapid increase in algae on a water surface.

Alternative energy sources Energy sources not derived from fossil fuels.

Amino acid Organic acid which forms part of a protein molecule.

Anaemia Disease of the blood which reduces its capacity to transport oxygen.

Anemometer Instrument that measures wind speed.

AONB Area of outstanding natural beauty.

Aquatic life Plants and animals which live in or near water.

Aquifer A porous rock which contains water.

Argon An element which exists as a gas in the atmosphere.

Artesian well A well which requires little or no pumping to obtain water which rises through a hole drilled through impervious rock.

Atmosphere A layer of gas which surrounds some heavenly bodies.

Atomic energy The energy involved with the nucleus of the atom.

Bacteria Microscopic organisms which are neither plant nor animal and contain no chlorophyll.

Bauxite A mineral ore from which aluminium is extracted.

Biodegradeable Substance which can be destroyed by living organisms.

Biomass The total weight of organisms in a given area.

Biological control The control of pest species by biological means.

Biosphere The part of the earth which is inhabited by living things.

Blast furnace Furnace for the extraction of iron from its ore.

Brackish water Water which contains less salt than sea water but enough to detect the taste.

Break crop A non-cereal crop grown to 'rest' a field which is usually sown with cereals.

Browsing The eating of leaves and shoots from the tops and side branches of trees and other large vegetation.

Calcareous soil A soil which is rich in calcium carbonate (lime).

Calefaction Pollution by increasing the temperature e.g. dumping hot water from power stations into the sea.

Calorie A unit of energy equal to 4.2 joules.

Carbohydrate Compound of carbon, hydrogen and oxygen. The hydrogen and oxygen atoms are in the proportion of 2 : 1.

Carbon dioxide A gas which forms 0.03% of the atmosphere.

Carnivore An animal that lives by eating other animals.

Carrion The flesh of dead animals.

Census The official collection of population details.

Chemical energy The energy involved in bonding atoms to form molecules.

City An urban area larger than a village, which has a cathedral.

Climax vegetation The last stage in plant succession – should last indefinitely.

Community The populations of plants and animals in a given area.

Conservation Caring for and developing for a modern need without destroying.

Contraceptive Device for preventing pregnancy.

Convection The movement in a gas or liquid caused by heating.

Conurbation A very large urban area often containing a number of towns with no countryside in between.

Country Park An area of the countryside with public access for recreational purposes.

Countryside Commission A government body which advises upon matters relating to the countryside.

DDT A non biodegradeable insecticide.

Decibel A unit of sound.

Deciduous Tree or shrub which bears no leaves in winter.

Deflected succession Natural plant succession which has been diverted by an external factor.

Demographer Person who studies human populations.

Desalination Removing salts from sea water to make it fit to drink.

Detergent Non-soapy cleansing substance.

Detritus Organic debris from decomposing organisms.

Dormant Alive but not growing or changing in any way.

Doubling time The length of time it takes for a population to double in size.

Drey The nest of a squirrel.

Ecosystem The physical environment together with all living organisms and the way they interact.

Effluent Liquid waste discharge.

Electrical energy Energy involved in the movement of electrons.

Encarsia formosa Parasitic insect used in the biological control of whitefly.

Energy The means of doing work.

Environment Surroundings – all aspects of the total area in which an animal (including man) lives and depends.

Equinox A day with 12 hours darkness and 12 hours light.

Eutrophication The addition of plant nutrients into an aquatic environment which upsets the ecological balance by reducing the amount of dissolved oxygen.

Factory farming Keeping very large numbers of farm animals or birds on a small area and purchasing all feeding stuffs.

Fallow Land which is cultivated, but not cropped, to improve its fertility.

Fertiliser Chemical substance added to the soil to increase crop yields.

Fertility The structure and nutrient content which determines the ability of a soil to produce a crop.

Floc Suspended solids clustered into groups.

Flocculation Particles in suspension grouping together to form crumbs which sink.

Food chain Chain of organisms through which energy is transferred as each organism eats its predecessor.

Food web An amalgamation of all the food chains in a natural community.

Fossil fuel Fuels formed from plants and animals that became buried in the earth's crust (coal, oil, natural gas).

Fractional distillation A method of refinement of crude oil.

Fungicide Chemical substance that is used to kill fungi.

Galaxy A group of stars.

Gamma BHC An insecticide.

Geothermal energy The energy contained in hot rocks, hot springs and geysers.

Green belt An area of countryside adjoining a built up area upon which permission to build is unlikely to be given.

Greenhouse effect The trapping of heat by being transparent to short wave radiation and opaque to long wave radiation.

Gypsum Calcium sulphate.

Habitat A particular kind of environment inhabited by organisms.

Haematite Rock quarried for iron.

Haemoglobin Red pigment of blood which transports oxygen.

Half-life The time it takes one half of a radioactive substance to decay.

Hamlet A small group of houses in the country, without a church.

Hard water Domestic water supply which contains sufficient dissolved salts to reduce lather production from soap.

Heathland An area of natural vegetation with many low shrubs (heather and bilberry etc.) and few trees.

Hectare A unit of area ($10\,000$ m^2).

Herbaceous plant Soft-stemmed plant – as distinct from trees and shrubs.

Herbicide Chemical substance which is used to kill plants.

Herbivore An animal that lives by eating plants.

Honey dew A sweet sticky substance left on plants by sucking insects.

Humus Organic material in soils which is in the final stages of decay.

Hydrocarbons Compounds composed of hydrogen and carbon (e.g. oil).

Igneous rock Rock formed by cooling and setting of molten material called magma.

Impervious Water cannot pass through.

Inorganic Substance that has never lived.

Insecticide A chemical substance which is used to kill insects.

Insectivore Animal that lives by eating insects and other invertebrates.

Intensive farming Farming for a very high production from a limited area.

Invertebrate Animal with no backbone.

Ion A single atom (or group of atoms) which carries an electric charge.

Ionised The term used when a gas is wholly or partially converted to ions.

Ionosphere The upper part of the atmosphere where much of the gas is ionised.

Irrigation The watering of crops.

John Innes compost Mixture of loam, coarse sand, peat and fertiliser, for growing plants in pots and boxes.

Joule A unit of energy. The amount of work done when a force of one Newton moves through a distance of one metre.

Kinetic energy The energy a body has by virtue of its movement.

Landscape The natural scenery of an area.

Larva Molten rock, that rises from the mantle beneath the earth's crust, and solidifies into igneous rock.

Latent heat The heat involved with the change of state from solid to liquid; liquid to gas; liquid to solid; gas to liquid.

Leaching The removal of soluble substances from the soil as water passes through it.

Ley A crop of grass or grass and clover mixture sown to produce for a short period (1–4 years).

Limestone A sedimentary rock which contains a high proportion of calcium carbonate.

Listed building A building which may not be changed or demolished without the authority of the Department of the Environment.

Lithosere An area of plants colonising bare rock.

Loam A soil which contains a mixture of clay, silt and sand particles.

Magma Molten rock deep in the earth's crust.

Magnetite Rock quarried from iron ore.

Mantle The layer of material immediately below the earth's crust and extending to the outer core.

Marl A soil consisting of clay and lime.

Metamorphic rock Rock which was formed from other rock types as a result of heat and pressure.

Meteorite A piece of material which falls towards the earth from space.

Micro-environment A small area where the environment is different in some way from the larger environment, e.g. under a stone.

Milky way The galaxy which contains the solar system.

Molecule The smallest part of a chemical compound which can exist; formed from two or more atoms bonding together.

Monoculture The growing of a single crop.

Mortality Death rate.

Natality Birth rate.

National Park A large area of natural beauty to be preserved for the enjoyment of the public.

National Trust A voluntary body which preserves places of natural beauty and historic interest while allowing public access to them.

Natural check The reduction of a population by food shortage or disease.

Nature trail A short walk through places of natural interest along a fixed route.

Neon An element which exists as a gas in the atmosphere.

Newton A unit of force, defined as the force that acting for one second on a mass of one kilogram gives it a velocity of one metre per second.

Niche A food source and habitat within an ecosystem.

Nitrogen A gas which forms 78% of the atmosphere.

Noise Unwanted sound.

Non-renewable resource A resource (e.g. coal) of which there is a limited amount and which will eventually be all used up.

Nuclear power Power derived from nuclear fusion (or fission).

Oil slick A mass of oil floating upon water.

Omnivore An animal that has a diet of both plant and animal matter.

Ore A mineral deposit, which contains a metal or other substance in quantities which are economically workable.

Organic Substance which is living or has lived.

Ozone A gas, molecules of which are formed in the upper atmosphere, by the combining of three oxygen atoms.

Particulates Small particles of solids which float in the air.

Pasteurise Partial sterilisation by heating and cooling.

Permeable Water can pass through (rocks).

Pesticide Chemical substance which is used to kill pests.

pH The scale by which the degree of acidity is measured.

Photosynthesis Plant utilisation of light energy to convert water and carbon dioxide into glucose.

Plankton Algae and associated fauna which live in the surface layer of water.

Planning Authority The body which controls new building and the use of existing buildings.

Planning permission Authority required to build, extend or change the use of a building.

Plant succession Progressive change in a plant community towards a stable climax.

Pollutant A substance which causes pollution.

Pollution The introduction of a substance into an ecosystem which causes harmful change.

Pooter Jar for the collection of small invertebrates.

Population The total number of a certain species in a given area.

Population dynamics The study of changes in a population.

Potential energy The energy a body has by virtue of its position.

Predator An animal which kills other animals for food.

Primary consumer The first animal in a food chain.

Protein Complex organic substance which contains nitrogen and forms the basic material of living organisms.

Protein deficiency A condition caused by a diet with insufficient protein to maintain good health.

Protozoa Single celled organisms.

Quicklime Calcium oxide.

Radiation frost Frost caused by rapid cooling of soils on a cloudless night.

Radioactive A substance which emits rays and/ or particles capable of penetrating opaque bodies.

Raw material Substances grown (or extracted from the earth) which are to be used for manufacturing goods.

Recycle To reuse the materials from one article to make another (e.g. scrap iron is manufactured into other products).

Relative humidity The water vapour content of the atmosphere compared with the maximum which can be held at that temperature.

Renewable resources A raw material which can be replenished, e.g. wool.

Reservoir A store of water, often held by a dam.

Resources Anything the world supplies which can be used by man, e.g. coal, fish and natural landscape.

Respiration The obtaining of energy by living organisms from the breakdown of sugar.

Rhizome Underground stem (usually horizontal).

Ribbon development Building on land alongside roads giving rise to 'ribbons' of development.

Rodent Small gnawing mammal with strong incisors.

RSPB Royal Society for the Protection of Birds.

Sand Fragments of rock with a diameter between .02 mm and 2.0 mm.

Screen A filter.

Sea floor spreading Oceanic crust formed as two tectonic plates move apart.

Secondary consumer The second animal in a food chain.

Sedimentary rock A type of rock formed from sediments.

Sedimentation tank A tank in which water is held while suspended solids sink.

Seismometer Instrument which measures earth vibrations (e.g. after earthquakes).

Selective herbicide A chemical substance used to kill weeds and leave crop plants unharmed.

Sewage The liquid waste of a community.

Slag Waste from blast furnace (calcium silicate).

Slaked lime Calcium hydroxide.

Slick (oil) A mass of oil floating upon water.

Sludge The sediment of a settling tank.

Smog A mixture of smoke and fog.

Solar energy Energy contained in the sun's radiation.

Solstice The time at which the sun is furthest from the equator.

Solute A substance which is dissolved in a liquid.

Solvent A liquid in which a substance is dissolved.

Species An interbreeding group of plants or animals.

Specific capacity The amount of energy required to raise the temperature of one gram of a substance through one degree Celsius.

Spring Water flowing from out of the earth.

SSSI A site of special scientific interest.

Succession See plant succession.

Sweep net Net for collecting insects.

Tectonic plate A large section of the earth's crust floating on the mantle.

Territory An area held by an animal against others of the same species.

Top carnivore The last animal in a food chain.

Town An urban area larger than a village which has no cathedral.

Transect A line of vegetation selected for study.

Trophic level The energy level in a food chain.

Tropopause The boundary between the troposphere and the stratosphere in the atmosphere.

Troposphere The part of the atmosphere where temperature decreases with height.

Ultraviolet Electromagnetic waves just beyond the visible spectrum (wavelength shorter than violet light).

Village A small group of houses, and other buildings together with a church, usually in the country.

Virus Extremely small life form which can live only in other living things.

Vitamin Chemical substances which are essential (in small quantities) for certain body functions.

Warfarin Poison used against rodents.

Water table The level in the ground below which all available spaces are filled with water.

Whitefly A plant sucking species of insect which lives in greenhouses.

Index